"Oh how I wish *The Baby Companion* had been availa[...] [...] or even my third child home from the hospital. Jessica and Andrea have offered mothers both amateur and experienced—an absolute treasure! They have taken into account the physical, spiritual, mental, and emotional realities we all face when bringing a baby into our homes and lives, and have given us a resource that gives us permission to be great parents without the pressure of being perfect ones. You are going to LOVE this book!"

> —SHELLEY HENDRIX, FOUNDER OF CHURCH FOR CHICKS AND AUTHOR OF *WHY CAN'T WE JUST GET ALONG: 6 EFFECTIVE SKILLS FOR DEALING WITH DIFFICULT PEOPLE*

"With a faith-based approach from the authors, the expectant mother is offered practical medical information and guidance through her pregnancy in *The Baby Companion*. This book offers a wealth of information to the first time mother."

> —MARCY SCHORSCH, MOTHER OF TWO; VICE PRESIDENT OF COMMUNICATIONS, BETHANY CHRISTIAN SERVICES

"No matter how unique our parenting situations are, we all seem to have one thing in common—we know how to be the best mom for our child. I'm so thankful Mrs. Wolstenholm, Dr. Johnston, and Dr. Rupe have written *The Baby Companion*—a book that throws out all the cookie-cutter how-tos and embraces the freedom of letting go of the idea of perfection in parenting, helping us embrace the unique qualities in our babies. They inspire us as moms to let God lead our journey of mothering through that first year and beyond, rather than looking to our neighbor, friend, or the latest parenting book trend. God has equipped us with everything we need to parent our baby just the way he or she needs it. All we have to do is let the Holy Spirit guide us along the way. Mothers will not want to miss the insights and inspiration found in this helpful and practical book."

> —AMY FORD, CO-FOUNDER OF EMBRACE GRACE MINISTRIES AND AUTHOR OF *A BUMP IN LIFE: TRUE STORIES OF HOPE & COURAGE DURING AN UNPLANNED PREGNANCY*

"Jessica Wolstenholm, along with Dr. Johnston and Dr. Rupe, offers moms an inspirational resource in *The Baby Companion*. The book is simple yet thorough in guiding moms through the often overwhelming days of new motherhood. I wish I'd had this book when my babies were born!"

> —KELLY HANCOCK, MOTHER OF TWO, FOUNDER OF FAITHFULPROVISIONS.COM AND AUTHOR OF *SAVING SAVVY: SMART AND EASY WAYS TO CUT YOUR SPENDING IN HALF AND RAISE YOUR STANDARD OF LIVING AND GIVING*

"There's no one perfect way to raise a baby. Motherhood is an incredible journey with God, and it's refreshing to see a book that doesn't just cover the baby's development, but the mama's, too! In *The Baby Companion*, you'll find a wonderful, well-rounded guide for new moms dealing with everything they can expect during baby's first year. It covers all the medical and developmental issues month by month; but even more importantly, it gives great spiritual encouragement to help moms during the sometimes overwhelming first year. Mothers will be reminded that God is in this with them and he has all the answers they'll ever need! I love that it doesn't focus solely on baby but also on mama and her unique needs and fears during this time. It's loaded with great truth from the Bible and will help a new mom keep her focus on God and his promises. There are real-life stories from moms throughout, and each chapter closes with an insightful prayer for mom and the prayer concerns she might have. An excellent resource to add to your parenting library!"

—KATE BATTISTELLI, AUTHOR OF GROWING GREAT KIDS AND MOM OF CONTEMPORARY CHRISTIAN RECORDING ARTIST FRANCESCA BATTISTELLI

"I remember how overwhelmed I felt by the standard issue baby care book I received from our pediatrician when our oldest child was born. While it contained a lot of information, it was also cold, clinical, and impersonal. Oh, how I wish I had a copy of The Baby Companion all those years ago! Not only does it provide a wealth of knowledge for new parents, it also comes alongside those parents with scripture and prayer to meet the very real spiritual and emotional needs of parenting through infancy. Finally, a book that combines the confidence of expert advice with a grace-filled, non-judgmental approach that I am confident will be a blessing to many families for years to come!"

—MEGAN TIETZ, AUTHOR OF SPIRIT LED PARENTING AND BLOGGER AT SORTACRUNCHY. NET

"Well, they have done it again. A grand follow up to their first book, The Pregnancy Companion, The Baby Companion answers the 'I don't even know what to ask' questions. Whether you are a first time parent or you are making another run at the grand adventure of parenthood, these women have provided a comprehensive, easy-to-follow, step-by-step guide through baby's first year. You are going to love it."

—JOE MCGEE, JOE MCGEE MINISTRIES

"The practical advice mixed with medical guidance and everyday inspiration from the authors in this book is invaluable! I only wish I'd had a resource like this when my kids were babies."

—SAMI CONE, BLOGGER & MEDIA CORRESPONDENT

"The Baby Companion is jammed packed with not only useful, needed information, but also with stories that make you smile and sigh. You will find mostly everything you need to take off on this adventure of parenting within this book. I wish I'd been able to have something so concise, well-balanced, and heartfelt when I was a new mom. You'll not only learn from this book, but cherish it along with your new little one."

—MELISSA GREENE, MOTHER OF TWO, PASTOR OF WORSHIP AND ARTS AT GRACEPOINTE CHURCH, AND ARTIST.

The Baby Companion

A Faith-Filled Guide for Your Journey
through Baby's First Year

Jessica Wolstenholm
Dr. Andrea Johnston
with
Dr. Heather Rupe

LEAFWOOD
PUBLISHERS

THE BABY COMPANION

A Faith-Filled Guide for Your Journey through Baby's First Year

LEAFWOOD
P U B L I S H E R S

Copyright 2013 by Jessica Wolstenholm, Andrea Johnston, and Heather Rupe

ISBN 978-0-89112-356-9
LCCN 2012045083

Printed in the United States of America

All scripture quotations, unless otherwise indicated, are taken from the Holy Bible, New International Version®, NIV®. Copyright ©1973, 1978, 1984, 2011 by Biblica, Inc.™ Used by permission of Zondervan. All rights reserved worldwide. www.zondervan.com. The "NIV" and "New International Version" are trademarks registered in the United States Patent and Trademark Office by Biblica, Inc.™

Scriptures noted NKJV are taken from the New King James Version. Copyright © 1982 by Thomas Nelson, Inc. Used by permission. All rights reserved. Scripture quotations noted MSG taken from The Message. Copyright 1993, 1994, 1995, 1996, 2000, 2001, 2002. Used by permission of NavPress Publishing Group. Scripture quotations noted KJV are taken from the King James Version of the Bible. Scripture quotations noted NLT are taken from the Holy Bible, New Living Translation, copyright 1996, 2004. Used by permission of Tyndale House Publishers, Inc., Wheaton, Illinois 60189. All rights reserved.

LIBRARY OF CONGRESS CATALOGING-IN-PUBLICATION DATA
Wolstenholm, Jessica, 1976-
The baby companion : a faith-filled guide for your journey through baby's first year / Jessica Wolstenholm, Dr. Andrea Johnston, with Dr. Heather Rupe.
    pages cm
  Includes index.
  ISBN 978-0-89112-356-9
1. Infants—Development 2. Infants—Care. 3. Mother and infant. 4. Mother and infant—Religious aspects—Christianity. 5. Child rearing—Religious aspects—Christianity. I. Title.
  HQ774.W65 2013
  204'.41--dc23
                                                                                    2012045083

Author cover photo by Amy Conner
Cover design by Jennette Munger
Interior text design by Sandy Armstrong and Becky Hawley

Leafwood Publishers is an imprint of Abilene Christian University Press
1626 Campus Court • Abilene, Texas 79601 • 1-877-816-4455 • www.leafwoodpublishers.com
For current information about all Leafwood titles, visit our Web site: www.leafwoodpublishers.com

13 14 15 16 17 18 / 7 6 5 4 3 2 1

For Cooper—you are my greatest blessing.

—Andrea

For Joshua—you bring me sweet joy every day.

—Jessica

Contents

Acknowledgments

Thank you, Lord, that you care enough about the often crazy and mundane days of motherhood to breathe life into a project that exists to encourage mothers of newborns. We are honored that you called us to write this book. We place it in your capable hands. Do with it as you will.

Thank you to the amazing team at Leafwood Publishers for continuing to believe that motherhood is about grace and peace—available only in Jesus Christ—Leonard, Robyn, Gary, Duane, Seth, Ryan, Lettie, Phil, Mary, and Al.

Jessica would like to thank:

My husband Dave, who continues to bless me with his constant strength and heart of service in my life. You are an amazing daddy to our children. My sweet babies, Hope and Joshua, whose lives are a picture of God's faithfulness and goodness. You are both such precious and unique beings and I pray for wisdom daily to steward your lives well. My family and friends, whose love and support bless me daily—Mom, Dad, Rex, Danielle, John, Monica, Michael, Jason, Kris, John, Emerson, Jason, Terri, Elijah, Bella, Kristy, Stephanie, Sarah, AnnJanette, and Donna. Thank you Kathryn Helmers and Meredith Smith for helping to build the foundation for this grace-community of moms. Thank you Andrea for taking the ride with me this time around. I'm so thankful that moms can have a physician and advocate like you. Heather, your friendship and partnership has been a joy in my life. I am so thankful we can join together in bringing peace and balance to moms and moms-to-be. To the girls at graceformoms.com, thank you for sharing the words in your heart to help moms find true grace. Your life experience is a gift to all of us. And most importantly, thank you God—for making beauty from ashes along my journey to motherhood. Your love and grace sustains me.

Andrea would like to thank:

My husband Mark for encouraging me to write this book with Jessica and for being a caring husband and father. Also to Jessica for asking me to co-write and for making the experience fun. I pray that there are moms out there who will find peace and confidence because of this book. To my precious Cooper—mommy loves you so very much. I am grateful for every day that I am with you, and I am so proud you are mine. To my mom, Nelda, for instilling a love of caring for babies in me and for showing me the best parts of motherhood. I am a better doctor and a better mother because of you. To my dad, Dan, for letting me always be a daddy's girl, even at thirty-five. I love you. To my medical friends, especially Purva, Vrinda, Katie, Lisa, and Jen, for making the years of training fun. You helped make even the longest days bearable and pushed me to do my best. To Tosha, for always being my best friend and for being a sounding board for this book. You are a great friend and mother and I appreciate your input so much. To my work family, for allowing me to work with you to provide the best care I can for my patients. I am especially grateful for my fellow pediatricians who helped with revisions for this work. And for my patients and their families—not everyone gets to go to work every day and know beyond a shadow of a doubt what their purpose is. You make that possible for me. I love caring for you, and I hope that I've been able to provide comfort and nurturing when you needed it most.

Why *This* Baby Book?

When I had my first baby, I had grandiose ideas of what the first months of motherhood would be like. Don't get me wrong, I knew there would be sleepless nights and dirty diapers, but I thought, as with many other things in my life, that enough hard work and diligence would give me reasonable control of the little person that just joined my life. When that was not the case, I felt like a mothering failure. I spent so much of my time and energy trying to figure out what I was doing wrong and, worse, asking God what was wrong with my baby and why he wouldn't give me a break and make her cooperate. Blinded by a culture that has a quick-fix answer to every problem (especially in parenting), I knew the root issue was obvious—I was a horrible mother.

When my daughter was a few months old, I decided it was time to "sleep train" her (quotes used to emphasize the fact that I didn't know what I was doing). I used a very popular book on sleep training and scheduling as a guide, and I was determined to make it work quickly—just like the book promised. Otherwise, it would be a testament to my inability to mother my baby. One day, I put her down for a midday nap and left her room despite the fact that she started crying. I let her cry for a few minutes and then went in to reassure her. She kept crying. Enter baby's room, reassure with a gentle voice "you're okay, it's time to sleep," exit room, and repeat. This went on for about thirty minutes, at which time she began to scream, so I sat down on the stairs with my "baby bible" and began to cry myself.

Lord, what am I doing wrong? Please make her go to sleep. If she doesn't sleep at regularly scheduled intervals, then I must be unfit to be her mother. Why would you allow me to be a mother if I can't even get my child to go to sleep? Maybe this was a bad idea.

And then I clearly heard him say, "Put the book away."

So I did. And there was silence. Not another sound from her room. She was peacefully sleeping.

"I have given you everything you need to mother this child who is uniquely created to bless your life," he gently whispered to my tired and doubting heart. "My Holy Spirit is the perfect guide to understand what I am calling you to do as her mother."

Although I continued to follow some of its principles, I didn't refer again to that book (or to any method book, for that matter) throughout the first year of my daughter's life. In fact, I haven't even cracked open that book since my son was born a few months ago. With the Lord's help, I have been able to let go of the hope of perfection and the idea that there is only one way to do anything in mothering.

So why on earth would I have the gumption to co-write a book about baby's first year after admitting my aversion to baby books? It is our hope that this book would transcend the role of other baby books for you. Think of it as the un-book of baby books. There are many great books on the market that focus on the medical truths that will guide you through baby's first year. Those books are wonderful tools that offer helpful information as you travel the uncharted waters of motherhood. And there are many other books that promise you the be-all and end-all solution to every baby issue from sleeping to eating to immunizations. Those books may work wonders for some, but they are the ones that got my amateur mother heart into trouble. Those books gave me a deep desire to write this one. This is not a how-to book. I learned early on that while the advice and ideas given by others are valuable, every baby and every family is different, so what works for one may not be what's best for others. That's why, in this book, you will find the important medical information needed to guide you through baby's first year and answer the questions you will encounter along the way gently wrapped in reminders to ultimately let God lead your journey. He has every answer to your silliest and most serious questions. But his answers may be different for you than they were for your girlfriend because, after all, every mommy and every baby is different. As I said in *The Pregnancy Companion*, there are only a few nonnegotiables when it comes to parenting. Most issues are about personal preference and your unique circumstances. That is why God wants you to let his Spirit be your Baby Companion.

For this book, I have the privilege of partnering with an amazing woman I have known since college. Dr. Andrea Johnston is a great physician, an intelligent woman, and a fairly new mother herself. You will be in very good hands, gaining insight and sound information from this pediatrician mom. You can trust that the medical information in this guide is coming straight from the doc. Any spiritual, devotional, or practical material will be coming from me, Jessica, after lots of prayer and seeking God for exactly what he wants to say to encourage you.

A Note from the Doc

I never thought I would help write a parenting book. When asked by Jessica to co-write the follow-up to *The Pregnancy Companion*, I first thought it would just be a neat way to help out a friend. As we've worked on the book this past year, though, it has come to mean more than that to me. I see new parents every day in my office struggling with decisions about how to care for their child. I see the agony over even minor decisions affecting their child's care. *How do you make sure you do everything right as a parent?*

The bottom line is, parents always just want to do the "right" thing. The great news is that most of the time there isn't just one right answer. There are very few absolutes when it comes to parenting. For example, you should absolutely never shake a baby. This is a nonnegotiable that I don't think anyone could argue against. For most other issues in pediatrics, however, there is a huge range of what is acceptable and best for baby. As a new parent, you will see impassioned books, blogs, and online postings from people telling you that your child will suffer irreversible damage for these minor decisions. You'll feel as though you've been branded with the words "world's worst parent" if you do not go along with whatever their soapbox belief is. Especially on hot topics like circumcision, breastfeeding, vaccines, and co-sleeping, there is a mountain of information, and those who feel the strongest tend to be the loudest.

For those hot-button issues, you must decide what is best for your family and your baby. I will give you the information in this book that I believe is the most current and accurate from a medical standpoint. I will offer suggestions about daily choices that might help make the first year a little easier. But in the long run, does it really matter whether you choose to give your child a pacifier or not? Does it really matter whether you wean the bottle at exactly one year or not? The simple answer is no.

This book is about reassuring you. You *are* a good parent. You love your child more than anyone else in the world, and you are doing your best. Will every day be perfect? Of course not. Will you let your ten-month-old watch television from time to time? Probably! Don't let these things define you as a parent.

This book contains fundamental medical information and what to expect each month of baby's first year. Unless otherwise noted, our recommendations are based on the most current American Academy of Pediatrics (AAP) recommendations (at the time of this writing). Because recommendations may change from year to year as more research is completed, be sure to ask your doctor what she currently suggests for her patients when considering a particular issue. Baby stats are taken from the current World Health Organization (WHO) growth charts per the current AAP recommendation. We've purposefully used a range for stats to adequately express how different each child may be. Girls naturally tend to be on the lower end of this range, while boys will likely be in the middle to upper end of the range. The information contained in this book should not be used as a substitute for the medical care and guidance of your child's pediatrician. Each child is different, and your child's doctor may have different recommendations based on your child's unique circumstances. Use this book as a guide to formulate your own questions for your baby's doctor. Above all, trust yourself as a parent and always ask for help when you need it.

What You Will Find in This Book

More than anything, we pray that you will find grace within these pages. Our desire is to provide you with all of the important medical information you need to make the best decisions for your baby. At times, we will share our own personal stories and points of view. These are not meant to tell you how to do something. They are meant to give you real-life examples. We trust that as you walk with the Lord, he will guide you in exactly what to do in each and every situation for your baby—and you should trust that, too!

Throughout the book, we will refer to your pediatrician as *she*, not because we prefer female physicians but because Dr. Johnston is a she and we had to choose. We will refer to the baby as *he* throughout the book because both Dr. Johnston and myself have a little boy, so it just came out that way. The same information applies whether you have a sweet baby girl or boy at home (except of course when we are discussing the penis or vagina—but hopefully that goes without saying).

Each chapter will be broken down into the following sections to guide you along each month of baby's first year.

Baby Stats—Since babies vary greatly in weight and length, these stats will be approximates that tell you what to expect. The ranges we used approximately include children from the fifth percentile to the ninety-fifth percentile on the growth chart—wide extremes from exactly "average" or fiftieth percentile. Your baby may be bigger or smaller than these guidelines. Discuss any concerns about baby's size with your pediatrician.

Development Checker—Once again, we will use guidelines to help you understand the new and exciting things baby may be doing each month. On some of the developmental milestones we have purposefully pushed out the range of what is "normal," despite what a strict developmental pediatrician might say. Because we do not want to cause any unnecessary concern, some of the milestones listed give a little bit more leniency on timing compared to other sources. If you are concerned that your baby is not on track with what you read, discuss your concerns with your pediatrician, and remember—every baby is different.

Baby Care—We will discuss everything from feeding to diapering to bathing, keeping in mind that many of these topics are about preference rather than what's right or wrong. Dr. Johnston will give her recommendations based on medical truth and experience, but we'll leave room for you to determine what is best for your baby.

Expectations for Your Doctor Visits—In each chapter, we will discuss what you can expect at your next doctor's visit. Some months you will not visit the pediatrician (unless baby is sick), so we'll include other helpful information such as tips for communicating with your doctor and keeping track of baby's immunizations.

Common Questions You May Have This Month—Each month, we'll address questions that may be at the forefront of your mind.

Mommy Care—One of the most important factors in enjoying baby's first year is making sure you take care of yourself along the way. Dr. Heather Rupe (OB-GYN and co-author of *The Pregnancy Companion*) will be joining us at a few important points along our journey through the year to offer helpful information and advice for taking care of mommy throughout baby's early days (and beyond).

Real-Life Stories—Because every mother wants to know she's "not the only one," we will share a few stories and experiences from other moms who have dealt with different issues throughout baby's first year. Hearing how these women walked through difficult times and overcame obstacles will inspire your heart.

Crib Notes—At the end of every third chapter, you will find a summary of the previous three months that you can use as a "cheat sheet" for that stage of baby's first year. We'll include notes on baby's development, feeding, sleeping, and play, and a Scripture to encourage you throughout those months.

Truth for the Journey—Just as we did in *The Pregnancy Companion*, we will include encouraging verses and devotional thoughts to accompany you through the very exciting yet exhausting days of motherhood. We'll also include practical tips and ideas for planning, organizing, and even shopping for baby.

Before we get started, I want to take a moment to pray this prayer over you, my mothering friend. May these words bring you peace and godly confidence as you embark on this journey. Remember, you are not alone. Our faithful and gracious God is your Baby Companion.

> *Dear Lord,*
> *Thank you for the precious gift of life that you've given my friend. I ask you now to infuse her heart with your righteous confidence, the kind that only comes from walking closely with you. May she know you are near because she daily draws herself to you. Give her wisdom in every moment as she loves and cares for her little one. Lead her through every decision she encounters*

for her family. Cover each day with your grace so that she can do more than merely survive it. Most of all, I pray she would be able to cherish each day of her baby's first year, for they will pass too quickly.

In Jesus' name,

Amen

Grace and peace to you as you embark on this exciting journey,

Jessica

A Real-Life Story

A Note for Single and Military Moms

Katie, military mom to Audrey and Sarah

My husband joined the National Guard ten years ago, before we were married. Our pre-baby first deployment was hard, but our post-baby second deployment was even harder. While it's true that military moms have the homecoming to look forward to, long deployments make you feel like a single mother. I don't pretend to know what it's like to be a single mom in the typical sense, but I imagine many of the daily challenges are very similar. I hope my words will be an encouragement to both military and single moms.

Whatever the circumstances surrounding the fact that you are parenting alone during this season, God knows your situation and his heart is for you. He knows how hard it is to be both mommy and daddy—whether it be for a year or for an undetermined amount of time. He knows the strength that you need to make it through each day and—as this book will encourage you—that strength is available in him. He understands your fears and he is ready to replace them with his peace. He knows the longings of your heart and he wants you to put your hope in him.

Besides completely and utterly depending on God to get me through my days, here are a few practical lessons I have learned along the way:

Control what you can. For us "control freaks" this is really difficult. It took me two very long deployments to get this. Once I learned to find contentment and peace in the little details that I could control, it became an incredible survival skill.

Military moms—acknowledge that you can't control what he is doing "over there," you can't control what shape he comes home in, and you can't make the months march by any faster. Do this, and then come up with a daily routine and stick to it. Plan fun activities once a month to look forward to, pray when you are scared, and choose to celebrate each week or month that passes by instead of despairing at how long eight more months is going to be.

Routine is everything. Sure, there may be special occasions when a break in routine may be necessary, but for the general day to day, make it a point to set meal times, honor bedtimes, and keep the same house rules. As incredibly hard as it may be to sit in that pew week after week without a spouse, or create and maintain those fun family holiday traditions, do it! It will go a long way in giving young children a sense of stability and identity as a family even when dad can't be present.

Working moms—this may seem even harder when you are trying to perform at work and keep everything at home afloat. Seek the Lord for strategies to create routine for your family, and though you always feel short on time, do your best to make time for fun activities once in a while.

Cut yourself a break. There will be good days and bad. Some days will happily fly by, and even the fleeting moments of recalling that you are going it alone will fail to interrupt your fun. There will be days when you absolutely feel like "super mom." Then, there are those days when no matter how hard you try to put on a smile, be grateful for all you have in life, and tell yourself "he will be home soon" or "I will not be alone forever," time will feel like it is standing still. It will take your breath away. But take comfort in knowing that those feelings are normal. You have not somehow failed if you have a bad day. You are under incredible stress, and you are doing your very best in a very tough situation. So, grit your teeth, make it through the day, and once the baby is tucked in for the night (or a few hours), let yourself have a good cry. Feel the feelings that are coursing through you, and cry out to God. . . . He can handle it! Often, acknowledging your feelings and not letting them bottle up will allow the despair to pass with a good night's sleep and the start of a new day.

Find Support. Single mom or military mom . . . we need support. Once in a while, you may need someone to help with a home repair or errand, or to take the children off your hands for a couple of hours. Do not be afraid to ask those around you for help. Whether you look to family members, coworkers, or your church congregation, have your "extended family" on speed dial. Find other moms in similar situations and get together on a regular basis. Although your strength and grace comes from the Lord, he does not want you to be alone during this season. Find supportive people and lean on them.

Hope. The days of military moms and single moms are long and hard. The working and waiting wears the best of us down. Life does not always turn out the way we plan, but God covers us with great grace and redemption even when circumstances are outside of our control. As I said before, God knows the longing in your heart. He understands your every need. He loves you so much and he wants you to put your hope in him to walk with you and your child(ren) each and every day.

"'For I know the plans I have for you,' declares the Lord, 'plans to prosper you and not to harm you, plans to give you hope and a future.'" Jeremiah 29:11

"May the God of hope fill you with all joy and peace in believing." Romans 15:13

Baby's First Year at a Glance

Month	Size	Feeding	Sleeping	Milestones
1	6-10lbs 18-21in	BF: 20-30min/2-3hr FF: 3-4oz/3-4hr	Sleeps often, 30min-3hr through day with longer stretches at night	Responds to sound Able to lift head slightly
2	7.5-12.5lbs 20-23in	BF: 15-30min/2-3hr FF: 5-6oz/3-4hr 1-2 night feedings	4, 30min-3hr naps through day with longer stretches (6 hours) at night	Smiles, coos Can follow field of vision
3	9-15lbs 21.5-24.5in	BF: 15-30min/3-4hr FF: 5-6oz/3-4hr 1-2 night feedings	3-4 naps through day with longer stretches (6-8hours) at night	Recognizes faces Able to hold head up
4	12.5-19lbs 23-26.5in	BF: 15-30min/3-4hr FF: 6-7oz/3-4hr 1 night feeding	3 naps through day and may sleep through night with only 1 feeding	Learning to roll over Reaches for toys
5	13-20lbs 24.5-27.5in	BF: 20-30min/3-4hr FF: 6-7oz/4hr 1 night feeding	2-3 naps through day and may sleep through night with only 1 feeding	Plays with hands/feet Rolls over Grasps toys
6	14-21lbs 25-28in	BF: 20-30min/3-4hr FF: 6-7oz/4hr Starting solid foods	2 naps per day and may sleep up to 12 hrs through night now	Learning to sit up Stands and bounces when held up
7	15-22lbs 25.5-28.5in	BF: 4 times/day FF: 8oz 4 times/day Solids at mealtimes	2 naps per day and may sleep up to 12 hrs through night now	Babbles often Plays with hands, brings them together
8	15.5-23lbs 26-29.5in	BF: 4 times/day FF: 8oz 4 times/day Solids at mealtimes	2 naps per day and may sleep up to 12 hrs through night now	Sits with no support Learning to crawl Consonant sounds
9	16-23.5lbs 27-30in	BF: 4 times/day FF: 8oz 4 times/day Solids at mealtimes	2 naps per day and may sleep up to 12 hrs through night now	Scooting/crawling Says repetitive sounds
10	16-24.5lbs 27.5-30.5in	BF: 4 times/day FF: 8oz 4 times/day Solids at mealtimes	2 naps per day and may sleep up to 12 hrs through night now	Learning to stand May wave bye-bye Feeds self w/ fingers
11	17-25.5lbs 27.5-31in	BF: 4 times/day FF: 8oz 4 times/day Solids at mealtimes	2 naps per day and may sleep up to 12 hrs through night now	Plays peek-a-boo Cruising May say mama/dada
12	17.5-26lbs 28-31.5in	BF: 4 times/day FF: 8oz 4 times/day Solids at mealtimes	2 naps per day and may sleep up to 12 hrs through night now	May be walking Drinks from cup Uses objects correctly

Notes: Information reflects baby's possible progress by the end of each month. Sizes are approximate averages and are based on current AAP findings and WHO growth charts. All other information is meant to be a guide. If your baby falls outside of these ranges or examples, discuss your concerns with your doctor.

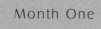
Baby's First Days

Say Hello to a Whole New Level of Love

If ever you thought you knew a deep level of love, becoming a mother will open your heart to a deeper well of emotion and connection than you have ever felt before. Holding a life within your arms that was meant to be there—purposed before the beginning of time—will do something extraordinary in you. All of your anxieties and fears can become overshadowed by the love you feel in your heart for this tiny, little life. What a wondrous gift—the connection between a mother and child.

As you adjust to a new life with your precious child in the months ahead, I pray your heart and mind would be turned toward the reality of this phenomenon of love. When your days get hectic or overwhelming, look deeply into baby's eyes and find the peace that comes in knowing you were destined to be the mother of this child. God has called you and therefore equipped you, with the help of his Spirit, to love and care for this life. It all starts with the deep level of love you feel for your baby. Everything your baby needs will flow out of that love.

We are so honored to be joining you on your journey through baby's first year. The days ahead will be filled with many ups and downs. Moments of pure joy will combine with those of complete craziness as you adjust to your new normal. We pray the information and encouragement within these pages will help guide you but ultimately point you back to the Creator of life who is your Ultimate Companion each step of the way.

Before You Leave the Hospital

Before you are released from the hospital, your baby will receive several tests to ensure he is ready to go home. These tests are routine and should have minimal, if any, effect on your baby. If you would like to be present for these screenings, please talk to your doctor or nurse. Every hospital has a different policy on how and when such tests are administered, so make sure you talk it over with them beforehand.

APGAR. The APGAR score (appearance, pulse, grimace, activity, respiration) is used to assess your baby's condition at one minute and five minutes of age (and sometimes at ten minutes or longer). The score is based on baby's color, heart rate, muscle tone, reflex response, and breathing. A low score may indicate the need for resuscitation assistance (supplemental oxygen) or chest X-rays. The score is not predictive of how healthy your baby will be as he grows up and does not indicate intelligence or ability in any way.

Newborn screen. The newborn screen is a mandatory state screening for multiple genetic diseases that can be life-threatening. For many of these congenital diseases, treatment can be as simple as a special formula or a special diet when taking solids. A small heel prick will draw a blood sample around twenty-four hours after birth. Results usually come within a week or two. You should alert your baby's doctor of any genetic diseases that run in your family before this screen is performed.

Bilirubin screen. The bilirubin screen tests for jaundice. For further explanation on this test, review the section on jaundice later in this chapter. This test is done in most hospitals on the day of discharge, or sooner if your baby's skin appears yellow.

Hearing screen. A hearing screen is performed on all babies prior to discharge from the nursery. The purpose of the screen is to rule out any congenital hearing loss that could be present at birth. Do not be alarmed if your baby does not pass this test in the hospital. Your baby's nurse may try the test multiple times and still not get a "passing" read. This is usually due to fluid and debris from birth that is still present in the ear canals, blocking the transmission and causing baby to fail the test or "refer." The doctor or nurse may use this term to let you know that your baby did not pass the test. Your baby may also "refer" simply because a newborn's ear canals are so small that the test does not work properly. If your baby does fail the hearing screen, do not panic. Your doctor or nurse will make an appointment to have the test repeated sometime in the first month after birth. Nearly all babies pass the follow-up test. If your baby still does not pass, he will need to see an audiologist for further evaluation. You should alert your doctor of a family history of deafness.

Circumcision. If you have a son, you will need to decide whether you want him to be circumcised. While there is some evidence that circumcision provides preventative health benefits, these benefits are not substantial enough for the AAP to strongly recommend that newborn males be routinely circumcised. Circumcision is completely a personal choice, often based on tradition in your own family. No matter whether you choose circumcision or not, your child will not be the "only one" in his class either way.

Circumcision, the removal of the foreskin of the penis, is a surgical procedure usually performed in the hospital in the days following birth. While some parents circumcise their son for cultural and religious reasons, many parents simply do so for personal hygiene, feeling that it is easier to keep a circumcised penis clean.

Other Instructions You Will Receive Before Discharge

Cord care. Believe it or not, there are several viewpoints when it comes to umbilical cord care. Your baby's pediatrician may recommend that you use rubbing alcohol to clean the cord with diaper changes. She may also recommend that you do nothing. Some research shows that just leaving the cord alone unless it becomes soiled is the best method. Some hospitals may use an antiseptic stain on the cord after birth to prevent infections (often it looks blue or purple). Do not be concerned if you notice the cord area appearing this color. Your nurses and pediatrician will review their recommendations with you and give you instructions accordingly before you are discharged from the hospital.

Circumcision care. Vaseline, Vaseline, Vaseline! There's no such thing as too much Vaseline when it comes to circumcision care. You will need to keep Vaseline (some doctors recommend using gauze as well) on your baby's healing skin for ten to fourteen days after the circumcision is performed. Sometimes the head of the penis can get a light yellow "film" of tissue as it is healing. This can easily be mistaken for pus. Although circumcision infections are not common, you should let his pediatrician know if you have any concerns.

Your baby will be seen by a pediatrician every day that he is in the hospital. This doctor may be the pediatrician you've chosen or (if your pediatrician does not make rounds in your birthing center) a staff pediatrician. Each day, she will come and examine your baby from head to toe. She will discuss with you any concerns she has and will also be there to answer any questions you might have. Having a new baby is stressful, and you may have a million questions. Don't hesitate to ask— even if your questions seem minor or silly. Sometimes these seemingly insignificant issues can pile up, leaving you feeling lost and helpless.

If you had a typical vaginal delivery, you should be cleared to go home two days after birth. If you had a cesarean section, you will likely need to stay an extra day as your body begins to heal. If your baby requires extra monitoring or is admitted to the neonatal intensive care unit (NICU), he may require an extended stay in the hospital. Assuming all is well with you and your baby, you both will be discharged from the hospital two to three days after birth with instructions for follow-up.

Don't be in a hurry to leave your hospital or birthing center. Many parents cannot wait to get their baby home and settled. This is understandable, but remember—in the hospital, you have the help of a trained medical professional who is there to ensure the complete comfort and safety of you and your baby. Enjoy it while it lasts!

Precious Little NICU Babies

Any baby born before thirty-seven weeks gestation is considered to be a preemie. If your baby is born between thirty-five and thirty-seven weeks, he may or may not need to be in the NICU after birth. Some babies born early do remarkably well and are able to be cared for in the traditional nursery. However, if your baby is very early or has any medical issues at birth, he may need to be transferred to a NICU for more advanced medical care.

Having a baby in the NICU can be extremely stressful. You may not be allowed to hold your baby at first if he is sick. He may have special monitors and machines at his bedside so the medical staff can assess more closely how he is doing. You will have a thousand questions and may not understand everything that is happening. Your neonatologist and NICU nurses will do their best to make sure all questions are answered and should accommodate as many of your preferences as possible regarding your baby's care.

Babies born prematurely may need to drink milk that is higher in calories than typical milk. Human breast milk and most commercially prepared formulas include 20 kilocalories (kcal) per ounce. To help your premature baby grow, the NICU may ask you to pump breast milk and add a special calorie additive to make the milk anywhere from 22 kcal to 30 kcal per ounce. There are also commercially prepared formulas that are higher in calories that may be offered. While breast milk is best for any baby, it is particularly important for premature babies and is a wonderful gift you can give your child to make him as healthy as possible. The logistics of feeding your NICU baby may become overwhelming, especially if baby's hospital stay goes beyond that of your own. If you are discharged before your baby, you may need to make multiple trips to the hospital daily to feed and bond with your baby. This can be a very stressful time for new parents—juggling life and hospital visits. Remember that God knew before your baby was even conceived that this would be part of your story. He will meet you in your place of need with abundant grace for these difficult days. Trust that he has a purpose for this time. It's okay to admit that this is very hard and even seems unfair. Be honest about your emotions. Lean into your spouse, family, and friends for help and support. Before you know it, your sweet baby will be home, and you'll be enjoying life as a family.

Babies that are premature may be at risk for health issues that can persist later in life. The most common issues are developmental delays, learning or behavior issues such as ADHD, and chronic lung disease. They may also be at higher risk for serious illness with common childhood infections for the first year or two. Your baby's pediatrician will monitor your child closely during well-child checkups to look for indications of these issues, as early intervention ensures the best possible outcome.

Baby Stats

Keep in mind as you read the baby stats throughout this book that we've purposefully used a range to demonstrate how different each baby may be. Just because your baby

falls outside this range, that does not mean there is something wrong. You should dis-
cuss any differences with your doctor.

There is a range of healthy sizes for newborns. Most full-term babies (born between thirty-seven and forty weeks) weigh somewhere between 5 pounds, 8 ounces (2.5 kg) and 9 pounds, 4 ounces (4.2 kg) in weight and 18 inches (46 cm) and 21 inches (54 cm) in length. A mom who smokes during pregnancy or who has high blood pressure may be at risk of having a baby that is smaller at birth. Gestational diabetes may result in a newborn that is larger at birth. Your OB-GYN probably monitored such factors during your pregnancy and may have predicted that your baby would fall outside the typical range. A newborn who is smaller or larger than the average range does well most of the time, but he might receive closer monitoring from doctors and nurses after delivery just to make sure there are no problems.

Babies are born retaining some extra fluid, so it is normal for a baby to lose weight during the first few days of life. Typical weight loss is around 7 to 10 percent of body weight, and most babies will gain this weight back by the time they are two weeks old. If your baby loses more weight than expected, your doctor may ask you to supplement his feedings with formula or expressed breast milk to make sure he is getting enough to eat within the first week or two.

Babies will gain an average of ⅔ of an ounce (20 to 30 grams) per day. They may grow 1½ to 2 inches in length and gain an inch in head circumference in the first month as well.

Development Checker at One Month

Typical Skills
- ❑ Responds to sound
- ❑ Stares at faces
- ❑ Focuses eight to twelve inches away
- ❑ Responds to soothing when upset
- ❑ Lifts head slightly when on belly

Concerning Signs

- ❑ No response to loud sounds
- ❑ Lack of weight gain
- ❑ Weak sucking ability

Your doctor may want to see your baby a few times during the first month to ensure that he is gaining an appropriate amount of weight. Lack of weight gain—or "failure to thrive," as it is often called—could be an indication of breastfeeding issues or may possibly be a sign of a congenital issue. It is important for baby's pediatrician to keep a close watch on him during this time. Do not be alarmed if your doctor wants to check your baby's weight a few times this month. Be thankful for a physician who cares enough to make sure he is thriving.

Your baby's ability and tendency to suck is one of his most primitive neurological reflexes. If you bring baby to breast and he is unable to suck adequately, it could, in rare cases, be an indication of developmental issues. It is important not to confuse baby's latch issues with weak sucking ability. Many babies take time to learn how to latch on properly to the breast. But once there, they have a strong sucking reflex. Inform your doctor if you feel your baby is not sucking well.

Baby Senses

Sight. The typical range of your baby's best vision at birth is eight to twelve inches. This is about the distance between your face and your baby's face while he is latched on to breastfeed. Isn't that perfect? This is a wonderful example of how God created your baby perfectly to look to you for nurturing. Your baby will have difficulty seeing objects more than one foot away. In fact, you may notice that he looks cross-eyed when trying to focus on something. This is perfectly normal and should resolve by the time he is a few months old. As long as the crossing is transient and only lasts for a few seconds, there is no need for alarm. If he has one eye that tends to stay crossed, discuss it with your pediatrician. Babies have not developed the ability to see the full spectrum of colors yet, so his vision is mainly in black, white, and shades of grey. He may be very interested in looking at high-contrast patterns as early as two weeks of age. Color vision develops over the first three to four months of life.

Smell and taste. Research has shown that through a baby's senses of smell and taste, he can distinguish breast milk from other fluids. Babies tend to have a sweet tooth and show preference to breast milk and sugar water over more bitter smells and tastes. Sugar can have analgesic effects on babies, providing pain relief, which is why your doctor may ask you to breastfeed or give him drops of sugar water in the hospital after painful procedures such as blood tests and circumcision.

Hearing. After hearing his mother's and father's voices for the past nine months, your baby will soon be able to recognize your voices apart from others. He will have a hearing test in the nursery, as outlined earlier in this chapter. You may notice him startle to loud sounds. This is a normal reaction for babies, who are often hearing certain sounds for the first time.

Touch. After swimming in warm fluid for nine months, your baby's sense of touch may be quite sensitive at first. Many babies hate being cold and may cry during baths, diaper changes, or clothing changes. Holding your baby close to you will provide him warmth and give a sense of security that he will love. He may also like to be swaddled in a soft blanket.

Baby's Vision Development*

Age	Development
Birth	Though blurry, baby can see 8–12 inches in front of his face.
Newborns	Baby can see bright colors, faces, and large shapes. He will enjoy high contrast patterns.
3–4 Months	Baby begins to focus on smaller objects and can differentiate colors.
4 Months	Baby's eyes are working together and beginning to develop depth perception.
12 Months	Baby's vision develops to adult levels.

*Information taken from the AAP website healthychildren.org

Normal Newborn Behaviors

Newborn reflexes. The most common newborn reflexes are the *startle* and *rooting* reflexes. These reflexes are present at birth and typically disappear by four months of age. You may notice that your baby jerks and flails his arms and legs wildly in response to sounds. This is known as the startle (Moro) reflex and is very normal. This hypersensitive response to stimuli will typically go away in the first few months. Babies are also born with a rooting reflex, which aids in breastfeeding. They are made to be hungry and search for food. Your baby may nuzzle and "root" around your breast, even if you are bottle-feeding.

Periodic breathing. Like most moms, you may often find yourself staring at your baby while he sleeps, watching him breathe. Baby's breathing may be quick and shallow, then slow, then stop for a moment, and then resume again. Do not be alarmed if his breathing patterns become quiet or slow, or even if he seems to stop breathing for a few seconds. This is called "periodic breathing" and is completely normal. If you are concerned that he has truly stopped breathing, touch him gently to see if he responds. If baby does not respond, begin administering CPR immediately. If someone else is with you, have him or her call 911. If you are alone, administer CPR for two minutes, call 911, and then start again.

Coughing and sneezing. Your baby may seem to sneeze or cough often during the first few days of life. This is another normal newborn behavior—they are working to clean out their nose and throat after birth. Unless these actions interfere with breathing, sleeping, or feeding, there is no cause for alarm. Your baby may also sound congested off and on throughout the day. This does not necessarily mean he has a cold or is allergic to something in his environment. Many babies experience what doctors call "normal newborn congestion" due to the swelling of the nasal passages after birth. If he is not showing additional signs of illness, he is likely experiencing this normal newborn condition.

Hiccups. Babies tend to hiccup often after feeding. Although your child will experience hiccups throughout his life, they will not be as frequent by the time he is two to three months old. Hiccups do not bother newborns and do not need to be stopped. The best thing to do is wait it out.

Baby Care

Feeding

Current studies have proven that breast milk is the best and most natural nutrition you can give your baby. Breast milk is perfectly made to give babies exactly what they need to grow and flourish. Breastfeeding has numerous benefits for both mom and baby. First, breastfeeding creates a wonderful bond between you and your little one. For moms, breastfeeding provides a decreased incidence of certain female cancers such as breast and uterine cancer. This is thought to be due to the positive hormonal influences associated with breastfeeding. Since making breast milk requires energy, your body may burn extra calories and help you return more rapidly to your pre-pregnancy weight. For breastfed babies, there has been shown to be a decreased incidence of allergies, obesity, and gastrointestinal problems. Even a higher IQ has been linked to babies who are breastfed.

If your hospital or birthing center has lactation consultants on staff, be sure to accept as much help as they are able to give. Lactation consultants are invaluable in establishing good breastfeeding habits right from the beginning and making sure that your baby is latching properly. You will learn multiple holding techniques—try them all and see which position feels the most comfortable for you and your baby. It is recommended that you attempt to latch baby to the breast at least every three hours for the first few days. Even being awake is an early sign of hunger in a baby, so if he is awake, attempt to feed again, even if it has only been thirty minutes since his prior feeding.

The first few days and weeks of breastfeeding are hard. At first, you will only have drops of breast milk known as colostrum. Colostrum is an antibody- and nutrient-rich pre-milk that is unique to each mother. While most moms worry about their newborn "getting enough" to eat at first, the baby will have only drops of this milk for the first few days. You may experience minor pain when first latching and sore nipples from extended nursing. You will need lots of support from your spouse, family, and friends. It is easy to get discouraged because, as a mom, the most important task you feel you have in life is to feed your baby, yet you don't have any milk at first. I'm not sure why God made it so that a new mother's milk doesn't come in the first day. It sure would make things a lot easier. But he didn't. So you wait. And wait. And wait. Perhaps this is his way of encouraging new moms to become dependent on him from the get-go. About three to five days after birth, you will hopefully experience the relief of getting your milk in.

Unfortunately, few moms have the wonderful, instantaneous latch so often depicted in the lactation videos shown in prenatal classes. Contrary to what these superhero video moms show, most babies will not jump right onto the breast and start nursing with minimal effort. If you happen to have this experience, consider yourself one of the chosen few. If you have difficulty latching your baby at first, do *not* feel bad. Keep trying and try to keep a cool head. You will learn together over the next few weeks, and it *will* get better.

For some moms, day four or five comes and they still don't have any milk. This is what happened to me. My baby went from weighing 9 pounds, 9 ounces to 8 pounds, 9 ounces—a whole pound down. He was bright yellow from jaundice and starving. He was five days old, and I had nothing to offer him. I tried every old wives' tale in the book, including taking supplements such as fenugreek, prescription metoclopramide (Reglan), and raw baker's yeast. I would have done anything to have made my milk come in more. I latched him on every one to two hours around the clock and used a hospital-grade pump in between. And still, I was only getting drops. Add to this my day four hormone tidal wave, and I was a sobbing, crying mess. The harder my son cried, the harder I cried, too. I sought answers online and in books, finding a common theme—if I would just "relax," my milk would come in.

But how could I relax? My baby was starving! Thankfully, I had some pediatrician friends who came to my rescue. They sat me down, looked deep into my crazed eyes, and gave me permission to give my baby what he really needed—milk in any form possible. So I made him a bottle of formula, just knowing it would ruin his life forever. (That's what you hear, right?) I could hear the formula hitting his empty stomach and echoing like rainwater dripping into an empty barrel. I've never felt so guilty in all my life. I'm a pediatrician—if anyone should know she needs to breastfeed, it's me, right? But after he ate and I saw him finally relax and rest, I started to let go of the guilt.

Over the next few days, he slowly began to gain weight. I was still latching him and pumping as much as I could, but supplementing with formula as well. He was happy. I was happy—well, I was still a little crazy, but I was happier than I had been the week before.

I continued to pump and latch as much as possible over the next week. On my best day, at about three to four weeks postpartum, I pumped 6½ ounces total in a little over twenty-four hours. I was elated—two bottles' worth of milk. Slowly, though, my milk supply lessened and lessened, and when he was seven weeks old, I woke up one morning and was completely dry. My breastfeeding days were over. My husband can tell you I was quite emotional over what I considered to be a huge failure. But I knew that all God would ever expect from me as a mom (and therefore all I should expect of myself) is that I do my best. I really held on to this—yet I still allowed myself to mourn for an experience that I had wanted so badly.

I hope that every new mom will find encouragement and support, no matter what food you choose to give or are able to give your newborn. Of course, I encourage the mothers in my office to breastfeed right from the start. I fight side by side with them to attempt every avenue to get their milk established. I cry with those that cannot. I support those who are unable to breastfeed for other reasons, or who simply choose not to. It really will be okay no matter what happens. If you are having difficulty or feeling guilty, you are not alone. Please talk to your pediatrician or OB-GYN and see what resources are available in your area. Some lactation consultants will see you as an outpatient after you leave the hospital. If you have pain issues or supply concerns, give them a call or make an appointment for additional support. You may also find a local lactation consultant that will come to your home and coach you one on one. Take whatever measures you find possible to fight for your ability to breastfeed.

A Real-Life Story

The Bond of an Adoptive Mom

From Dr. Rupe

Like many moms reading this, my journey to motherhood was not the smooth path I had envisioned. My pregnancy with my oldest son was high-risk, and shortly after delivery I learned a second biological child was not to be in my future. As I fell more in love each day with my son, I always, in the back of my mind, had the bittersweet knowledge that completing my family would be a challenge.

God is gracious and loving. He had a perfect plan for our family. As he completely removed the desire for pregnancy from my heart, he replaced it with the overwhelming ache to adopt a child into our lives. At first this was a relief, walking in the peace of God's will for my life. However, three years and three failed adoptions later, I wasn't so sure.

Early November 2009, my world changed forever. God supernaturally brought our second son into our world. As he joined our family, I was surprised at how quickly and deeply I loved him. I was expecting it to take more time to bond, since I didn't feel him kick inside me for months, but he was immediately our son. Like other second-time moms, I wondered how I could love him as much as my first-born, but my heart grew exponentially the day he became a part of our family.

Despite the peace I felt over the decision to adopt, I was worried bonding would be different since I couldn't breastfeed. But our bonding was perfect. I could just hold him as much as I wanted without worrying over sore nipples. There was no formula guilt. As a bonus, I could get a little sleep by rotating feedings, since I wasn't his sole source of food at night.

No. I wasn't there for his first breath. But when the nurse placed him in my arms for the first time, he took my breath away, and he has a million times since.

More on Breastfeeding

A sudden influx of milk can lead to complications such as those discussed below. Your doctor will want to know right away if you think you have one of these conditions so you can be treated appropriately.

Engorgement. Breast engorgement is a common issue for breastfeeding moms. Engorgement, or a painful fullness to the breast, occurs when your breasts are adjusting to your baby's feeding demands or when it has been too long between feedings. Feeding your baby frequently on demand will help prevent engorgement from taking place. If your baby is eating frequently and you still feel engorged, you may need to take additional measures for pain relief. If you have a breast pump, sometimes pumping off a little milk and storing it can relieve some of the pressure. A hot shower or warm compress may help relieve mild pain; for more significant pain, sometimes a cool compress or ice packs are more helpful. Cool cabbage leaves placed on the breast are an old but effective method of pain relief.

Mastitis. Mastitis is another painful condition that some moms experience. Mastitis occurs when a portion of the breast does not drain properly. Bacteria may build up in the breast tissue and lead to an intensely painful infection. Symptoms of mastitis include pain, redness, and bumps on the skin of the infected breast. Some moms may also have a fever or even describe flu-like symptoms. I have had more than one mother describe the pain as "like a heart attack." You should alert your OB-GYN right away if you are having any of these symptoms. Treatment for mastitis includes antibiotics, pain medication, and a warm compress. Your doctor may tell you to nurse or pump more frequently during an episode of mastitis. It is important to do this so that your breasts will drain properly and the infection will not spread. Most current research shows that it is perfectly safe to continue breastfeeding even during an episode of mastitis. Your doctor will tell you if she wants you to "pump and dump," depending on your symptoms and what medications you are being treated with.

Thrush. While breastfeeding is almost always uncomfortable at first, the pain should subside after two to three weeks. If the pain recurs after this time it could be thrush (yeast infection of the breast). Women with thrush experience extremely sharp pain as the baby latches. They often describe it as feeling like hot knives are stabbing them in the breast. Additionally, their nipples will often be bright red in color. No fever or breast masses are present with thrush. The baby will often also have thrush, which is characterized by a white coated tongue. (Read more on thrush in babies in Month Six). Treatment includes oral anti-fungal medication, topical cream, and having the infant treated for thrush. It is key to continue oral anti-fungal medication for one week after the symptoms have resolved in order to prevent recurrence.

Knowing whether or not your baby is getting enough to eat is always a concern for breastfeeding moms. Unlike bottle-feeding, where you can see how many ounces your baby is taking, breastfeeding requires you to look at different cues to make sure your baby is getting adequate nutrition. The most basic cue is weight gain. If your baby is gaining 2/3 to 1 ounce each day, your supply is good. This is why your doctor may require more frequent weight checks in the first few weeks of life. Another reassuring sign will be at least four to five wet diapers per day. Your baby may have multiple bowel movements per day, or may only have one every other day or so. Let your pediatrician know right away if he shows signs of jaundice or seems overly sleepy, as these may be warning signs of inadequate milk intake.

Common over-the-counter medicines that are safe with breastfeeding include:

- Acetaminophen (Tylenol)
- Calcium (Tums)
- Prenatal vitamins
- Dextromethorphan (Delsym and Robitussin)
- Guaifenesin (Mucinex)
- Benedryl
- Mylanta
- Colace
- Milk of Magnesia
- Metamucil
- Fibercon
- Loperamide (Imodium)
- Cough drops and throat lozenges
- Ibuprofen

If you are able to breastfeed exclusively, your doctor may recommend that your baby receive supplemental vitamin D. No matter how much vitamin D a mom takes in, this nutrient simply does not pass sufficiently through breast milk. A vitamin D deficiency can cause skeletal problems such as rickets—a condition in which bones do not properly calcify and develop, resulting in curved, frail bones. Therefore, it is very important that babies receive their recommended daily amount.

Exclusive Pumping

Many moms desire to give their baby breast milk, yet, despite their valiant efforts, are not able to achieve success with baby to breast. In this case, some moms find exclusive pumping to be the perfect solution. With a steady schedule of pumping six to seven times per day (on average), your milk can become well established. Storing your milk and bottle-feeding will require more effort than traditional breastfeeding, but these small tasks can be offset with the ability to have others feed your baby from a bottle. Often, moms who find this method best for them end up with so much milk they choose to donate it. Ask your doctor or local breastfeed-ing groups/lactation consultants for more information on donating breast milk.

If you are struggling to breastfeed your baby, consider this alternative once you've worked through all other possible solutions. Talk with your OB and local lac-tation consultant as you think through this option. You may feel that this method of breastfeeding will allow less of a bond. Many moms I've talked to who have exclu-sively pumped felt a wonderful bond with their baby as they were able to look straight into baby's bottle-drinking eyes, knowing the milk they were receiving came from within them. Whether you are able to breastfeed traditionally, pump exclusively, or formula feed, your baby will thrive receiving his nutrition from a loving mom who is committed to meet his every need.

Formula- or Bottle-Feeding

If you are unable to breastfeed, you will need to choose which formula you want to give your baby. Some hospitals have contracts with formula companies and will automatically start your baby on the formula they use, so let the nurses know which brand you prefer. If it is different from the brand they keep on hand, you may need to provide your own, so check with the hospital beforehand and be prepared to bring some with you when you deliver. We discourage moms from frequently changing formulas, as it takes several days for babies to adjust to a new formula. You have to give their tummies time. Although generic formulas are cheaper than premium formulas, there are differences, and your baby may not tolerate the generics as well as he would the premium varieties. Ask your pediatrician what her preferred brand is and start there. Remember that your baby's digestive system is continuing to develop even after birth. It may seem as though he is intolerant of the milk you are feeding him, when in fact he just needs time to get used to this "new food." You should discuss any concerning symptoms such as gassiness, spitting up, or constipation with your pediatrician. Changing formulas may or may not help alleviate these symptoms.

There are over-the-counter medications for colic and gassiness that may be helpful. Talk to your doctor about the symptoms you are observing in your baby and ask what she would suggest. Unless your baby has significant gastrointestinal reflux and your doctor has recommended it, we discourage adding rice cereal and other thickeners to formula. New moms are tempted to do this because they have heard it may help their baby sleep through the night. Studies have shown, however, this is not actually true. Cereals and other thickeners can have other unwanted side effects such as constipation. In addition, the excess calorie load can make babies gain weight more quickly than they should.

On average, a full-term newborn will take only ½ to 1 ounce per feeding for the first couple of days. Remember, if you were breastfeeding, you would only have drops of colostrum during this time. So don't overdo it—babies were not designed to tolerate large amounts of milk in their first days. If your baby is spitting up, try reducing the volume of his feedings. Then you can slowly increase the amount of formula you are giving him over the next one to two weeks. Most babies by two weeks of age will take 2 to 3 ounces per bottle every two to four hours. You can find tips on formula preparation and organization in Month Three.

Typical Formula Feeding Patterns

Days 1–3: Start out slow! Remember, if you were breastfeeding, you would only have drops at this point. About ¹/₂ ounce to 1 ounce every two to three hours is typical.
Days 4–6: Increase slowly now as your baby is past the transitional period after birth and getting more alert. 1¹/₂ ounces to 2 ounces every two to three hours.
Days 7–30: Typically, babies will increase by about half an ounce per feeding each week now. If last week he was taking 2-ounce bottles, this week offer him 2¹/₂ ounces, and next week increase to 3 ounces per bottle, and so on. By the time babies are one month old, most are taking 3 to 4 ounces per feeding every three to four hours.

Typical Breastfeeding Patterns

Days 1–3: Attempt to latch every time baby is awake with a minimum of once every three hours. How long he feeds does not matter; at this point, it is more about stimulation and practice.
Days 4–6: Your baby should be getting hungry and aggressive. Latch him every two to three hours for ten to thirty minutes total on one or both breasts. It is perfectly fine for your baby to cluster feed during the day and throughout the night as well.
Days 7–30: Latch baby every two to three hours for twenty to thirty minutes total on one or both breasts.

Burping

Don't get too caught up with burping. Some babies burp well, but some do not. Every baby is different, and it is not cause for concern if your baby doesn't burp with every try. You should attempt to burp your baby every one to two ounces. This may help prevent some discomfort and spitting up. There are several methods for burping a baby. Your newborn nurse may have gone over these techniques with you in the hospital. The most common method is to hold baby over your shoulder and gently pat his back. Another option is to sit baby up in your lap after feeding, holding his chest and chin gently with one hand while patting his back with the other.

Sleep and Schedules

While staying in the hospital nursery, your baby may be put on a strict feeding and sleeping schedule. This is typically every three hours. However, at the end of his first week, your baby may seem like he wants to eat every hour. This is very normal. Allowing a newborn to "cluster feed" on demand, especially if he is breastfeeding, is suggested. Although a strict schedule might be nice, most babies won't cooperate with a rigid routine the first few weeks.

In addition to eating habits being less routine, your baby's sleep habits will likely vary in the first few weeks. A newborn baby may sleep for up to sixteen hours per day. Thus, a predictable schedule will be unlikely for the first month or two. Naps may last anywhere from thirty minutes to three hours. It is best to spend the first month or two learning and following your baby's cues. Additionally, most babies will have their days and nights mixed up for a while. Establishing a bedtime routine will help your baby learn the difference between day and night. We will talk more about bedtime in Month Three. For now, don't be surprised or disappointed when baby is up a lot at night. With patience and gentle leading, he will eventually fall into a more predictable routine when he is ready.

If your baby is having trouble falling asleep, swaddling may help. Understandably, a baby must adjust to life outside of the womb without warm and cozy protection around the clock. Swaddling your baby in a snug and breathable blanket may help settle him. The most common technique for swaddling includes these simple steps:

1. Lay a blanket on a soft, flat surface.
2. Fold down the top corner so it points to the middle of the blanket.
3. Lay baby's head on the folded corner.
4. Wrap the bottom corner over baby's feet (not too tight).
5. Pull one side corner of the blanket over baby's body. Tuck in snugly around baby's opposite side.
6. Pull the opposite corner over baby's body, tucking it snugly around his side.

Your baby should now look like a sweet little burrito.

Note: The AAP warns against swaddling a baby too tight. If baby's legs are straightened out and he is swaddled tightly in this pike position, it can lead to hip dysplasia. The bottom of baby's blanket should be just roomy enough so baby can flex his hips freely if needed. A good swaddle is tight enough for the blanket to not loosen and cover baby's face yet loose enough to allow for some movement.

Soothing

The 5 S's. Dr. Harvey Karp, author of *The Happiest Baby on the Block*, developed a technique he calls "The 5 S's of Soothing." His recommendations include five different techniques that he believes are most effective for soothing a newborn: swaddling, side/stomach position (while awake only), shushing sounds, swinging, and sucking. These timeless methods may help calm your baby if he is upset. They are invaluable to mothers who have babies with colic (see the common questions in Month Two for more on colic).

Co-sleeping. Where baby will sleep is a highly controversial topic for many new moms. Even the word "co-sleeping" can electrify a discussion between friends. However, in many parts of the world, co-sleeping is not controversial at all. It is very much the norm. While the likelihood of SIDS is low with co-sleeping, current research still shows that the safest place for your newborn baby to sleep is in the room with you, but in his own space. Whether you use a bassinet or a crib, make sure that there are no blankets, toys, or bumpers that could become loose and cover your baby's face.

Co-sleeping a newborn baby directly in the same bed as a parent is not recommended. SIDS risk is most increased if there are smokers in the home and if the parent is impaired in any way—whether from medications, alcohol, or just extreme fatigue. If any of these are true, you should *not* co-sleep with your baby.

Sudden Infant Death Syndrome (SIDS)

SIDS is the leading cause of death for infants under one year of age. It is most common during the second through the fourth months of life. The risk decreases between months four and six after baby learns to roll over, and typically disappears between months nine and twelve. Risk factors for SIDS include smoke exposure and tummy sleeping. Breastfeeding and back sleeping reduces the incidence of SIDS. SIDS is not caused by immunizations, choking, or gagging during sleep. Always remember to put your baby on his back to sleep. The American Academy of Pediatrics began recommending this sleep position in 1992. Since then the annual SIDS rate has declined more than fifty percent.

As a physician, I feel one hundred percent obligated to give parents the data regarding co-sleeping and the risks that come with it. But let's assume for a moment that there isn't any SIDS risk with co-sleeping. One of the most frequent questions I am asked at the eighteen-month checkup is, "How do I get my child to sleep in his own bed?" Often, parents are expecting their second child at this time, or at least thinking about baby number two. All of a sudden, you need to transition the first kid out of the bed to make way for the next one. Most of these moms haven't slept eight hours straight since their first baby arrived—sleeping next to a child often means restless sleep. So, even if there were no possible risk factors, I would still caution parents about the practical consequences of this nightly ritual. Co-sleeping is a *very* tough habit to break at two or three years old. I know many parents who endure weeks of torture getting their toddler or preschooler transitioned into his own room. It may be best if you don't start the habit at all.

If you enjoy having your little one close to you at night or simply believe it's a matter of survival to have baby near when you are feeding him a few times a night, then I recommend finding a safe tool for allowing baby to sleep close to you (such as a co-sleeper bed). If you truly enjoy having a "family bed" and want to continue as your children get older, it's your decision. Most parents would not want a five-year-old in their bed every night, kicking them in the ribs. But if it doesn't bother you, then medically, it's perfectly fine for older children and may be a wonderful bonding experience for your family.

Diapering

By now you've chosen whether you will use cloth or disposable diapers for your baby. This decision is a personal one, often influenced by preferences. There are no medical reasons for either cloth or disposable diapers. The decision often depends on how green or frugal a family is.

There is truly no clear answer to the question of how many wet and dirty diapers per day a baby should have. Obviously, having lots of wet diapers indicates that he is getting plenty of fluids and is not dehydrated. But I've learned that the definition of a "wet" diaper varies. When we first brought my son home from the hospital, my husband was captivated by the moisture-sensing line on our son's diapers. Any change from yellow to blue, and he was getting a diaper change. Then he chilled out after a few weeks (after realizing how expensive his little obsession was) and, unless our baby was fussy, we waited until his diaper was moderately wet before he was changed. It can be challenging for either a parent or a physician to truly determine if your baby is making enough wet diapers. Parents can tell me that they've "only changed two wet diapers today," but that may in reality be the same urine output as another baby whose family tells me he had five wet diapers. It just depends on how often you change them. The bottom line is, your baby should probably have some urine output after each bottle. It may be a lot or just a little. If you truly feel that he is not making enough urine and there is something going on that could point to dehydration (your breast milk is not in yet, he will not latch to your breast or the bottle, or he is vomiting every feeding), you should notify your doctor immediately.

Perhaps because of the evident obsession with baby poop found all over the Internet, new moms are often concerned about the color and consistency of their baby's stool. During the first twenty-four hours of life, your baby's bowel movements will be sticky, black stools called meconium. Babies' stools then transition to be a range of colors. There is no "right" color. Stools in a newborn can range from yellow to green, and orange to brown. They may be liquid and appear to have seeds (especially in breastfed babies) or may be more formed. The range of normal is very wide. If your baby hasn't pooped in twenty-four hours, it does not necessarily mean he is constipated. Even some breastfed babies only poop once every one to two days. Babies will often grunt, draw up their legs, and strain when having bowel movements. This is not always a sign of constipation. If your baby is having very hard or abnormally large stools, or is crying in pain with bowel movements, you should notify his doctor right away. These are signs of constipation, and your pediatrician can give you recommendations on treating these symptoms. Babies that are formula-fed, particularly those taking soy milk or added rice cereal, are at higher risk for constipation. Treatment may include additional feedings, adding corn syrup to his bottle, or giving him a small amount of juice or water. Adding a tablespoon of corn syrup to a bottle or giving your baby two ounces of juice will draw water into the bowel to soften the poop that is currently there. These treatments work as a natural laxative for baby.

Be careful not to secure baby's diaper too tight or it could upset his tummy. As a general rule, you should be able to slide your fingers under the top of baby's diaper even after securing the tape (or pins/fasteners).

Bathing

Only a sponge bath should be given until baby's cord detaches at about two weeks of age. You should not get the umbilical cord wet. If the cord does become soiled with stool from a diaper, you may clean it gently with a damp washcloth, but do not soak the cord with water. Babies may be bathed every day or less often, depending on a parent's preference. Commonly, moms will choose to bathe their baby every other day.

Babies with sensitive skin may need to be bathed less frequently and will require fragrance-free and dye-free bath products. Many baby bath products are highly scented with lavender or other fruit or floral scents. These fragrances and dyes may be too harsh if your baby has sensitive skin, or even if he doesn't, so use any products with fragrance and dye with caution. Babies with sensitive skin will develop dry, scaling or flaking skin and sometimes larger patches of dry, red eczema as well. If your baby seems to have any skin irritation, you may see improvement with "hypoallergenic" products. Discuss any concerns about your baby's skin with your pediatrician at your next appointment.

Cradle cap. Cradle cap is a common problem in newborns. This flaking of the scalp usually appears at a few weeks old and looks like dandruff in mild cases. Babies with more significant cradle cap may have thick, greasy-looking scales on their scalp. Cradle cap may even cause some of baby's hair to come out. The most basic treatment is to use baby oil and a soft baby brush to gently brush out the flakes. Another helpful solution is to use a dandruff shampoo a few times per week. Cradle cap may be present throughout baby's first year and beyond. It is more of a nuisance than a cause for concern. Do what you can to limit this cosmetic inconvenience, but do not worry. As baby's hair grows in, it will likely cover any remnant of cradle cap, and before you know it, baby's scalp will be smooth and beautiful.

Jaundice. Jaundice is another very common condition in newborns that causes a yellow tint to baby's skin. Jaundice is a result of buildup in the body of a substance called bilirubin. Bilirubin is a normal byproduct of the breakdown of red blood cells. In infants, this chemical is not broken down as easily because of their naturally immature liver at birth. Jaundice may first appear on the face and then worsen to include the eyes, chest, and remainder of the body. Jaundice normally occurs on day three or four of life. Any jaundice in the first twenty-four hours of life is abnormal. Babies who are breastfeeding or those who have had birth trauma and bruising are at an increased risk of developing jaundice. Your doctor will watch closely for signs of jaundice and may run labs to check the baby's bilirubin level even prior to discharge from the hospital. High bilirubin levels over time are associated with problems of the nervous system, so it is important that your doctor is notified if you have any concerns about jaundice after leaving the hospital. Do not worry if you are told your baby has jaundice. When detected, it usually does not have to be treated at all. Just keep feeding your baby to make sure he is staying hydrated. If the bilirubin gets too high, it is very treatable with phototherapy ("special lights"), sometimes also referred to as a "bili blanket." Jaundice normally resolves in formula-fed babies by one week of age and in breastfeeding babies in two to three weeks.

Nail care. Moms are often scared to clip or trim their newborn's nails. This is understandable, since a baby's fingers are so tiny. It can be very unnerving to approach your baby's sweet little fingers with a sharp object. Hospitals will often give new moms baby nail files. The jury is still out on whether these soft emery boards actually work. Please resist the temptation to bite your baby's fingernails off. It might seem like a good solution, but it is actually unsanitary. Try your best to use a soft nail file or baby nail clipper. Clip baby's nails while he is asleep so there are no sudden movements. Gently press back the skin under his nails and file or clip each nail carefully. For our recommendation on the best baby nail clipper, see the Appendix at the end of this book.

Girl Talk/Boy Talk

Penis care. If your baby is uncircumcised, your job is easy. Just bathe and clean him as usual. You should not pull back on his foreskin at all. The skin will naturally start to retract in the next few years. You can teach him how to clean himself well after this skin has retracted on its own.

If he is circumcised, you will need to apply Vaseline to the penis for the first few weeks until the skin is healed. After he is healed, you should clean well around the head of the penis with each bath. If he has a little excess foreskin, you should pull it back slightly so you can clean well underneath this skin. Often, a baby will have a significant fat pad on his groin above his penis. This fat pad may push skin back out over the shaft and head of his penis. Some babies even have a "hidden" penis because the fat pad is so significant. Do not worry—this is common. After he starts walking, running, and climbing, he will lose most of this baby fat, and his penis will look fine. Until then, gently push back this fat pad at bath time and with each diaper change to make sure you can clean around his penis well.

In some baby boys, you may not always be able to see his testicles dropped down into his scrotum. Most of the time, this is a normal finding and no cause for concern. Many newborn baby boys have what are called "retractile" testicles. Their testicles may be easy to see at times and then not at others. Usually baby's doctor can feel their testicles by gently pushing them down from their groin into the sac. Most of the time, the testicles will eventually drop down into place on their own. If your baby's doctor is unable to feel one or both of his testicles, she may order an ultrasound just to make sure that they have indeed descended.

Vagina care. Cleaning baby girls can be somewhat intimidating for new parents. For starters, newborn girls often have vaginal discharge that is quite noticeable. It may look like cloudy, white mucus coming out of her vagina. This is a good thing. It keeps her skin lubricated and soft. Sometimes, in the first week or so after birth, it may have a little blood in it. This is due to hormonal shifts (similar to the way a menstrual cycle works) and is normal as long as it's just a small amount. At least once daily (or especially after a significant bowel movement), make sure you spread her labia apart and clean any soiling on her skin. You may wipe away any mucus or stool at that time.

Baby Safety

Shaken baby syndrome. Shaken baby syndrome occurs when a baby is shaken (usually out of frustration) for even as little as five seconds. This is a very serious issue that all parents should be aware of. Even moderate shaking is enough to cause damage to a baby. Shaking a baby can cause severe and permanent damage. Babies that have been shaken can experience blindness, seizures, mental retardation, and even death. If you are feeling frustrated due to your baby crying or not sleeping, you should put him in a safe place such as his crib or swing and then walk away. Go outside, take some deep breaths, and calm down. It is very common for the pressures of life with a newborn to overcome new parents. If you feel an overwhelming sense of frustration, the best thing for you and your baby is to walk away. Even if baby is inconsolable, he will be fine if you put him in a safe place and take a few moments to gather your composure.

Car seat. Hopefully you researched car seat safety to ensure your infant seat was safe and properly installed before you brought baby home from the hospital. Visit www.nhtsa.gov/Safety/CPS for more information on car seat safety and to find your state laws. It is not recommended to use strap covers or car seat inserts of any kind. Your baby's seat was tested and approved for use as-is. Adding all of those cute little accessories only alters the function of his seat. Unless your baby is a preemie, there is no real need to use padding. Your baby is much more comfortable in his car seat than you think.

Infant CPR. Having basic life support skills can be invaluable to a new parent in an emergency situation. Look for an infant CPR class at your hospital or local YMCA. It is a good idea to invite grandparents or other caregivers to participate in CPR classes with you. If you are unable to attend a class, the American Heart Association has created the Infant CPR Anytime Kit for at-home instruction. This tool is a great way for all family members to learn infant CPR. For more information, visit the American Heart Association website.

Changing table. Most babies do not try to roll over until about four months of age, but some attempt it sooner. Use your table's safety straps and never leave baby unattended on the changing table. Even though baby is not mobile at this point, it is better to get in the habit now of never walking or even looking away while baby is on a raised surface.

Crib. As mentioned earlier in this chapter, make sure there are no loose blankets, soft toys, or crib bumpers that could cover baby's face while he is sleeping. Even though babies do not move around the crib much at this stage, it is best to keep his sleep space clear of anything that could be a danger. Refer back to our discussion on swaddling if you are concerned that baby may be cold while sleeping. You may also consider using sleep sacks as an alternative to blankets and swaddling. These safe, convenient, wearable blankets are often used in hospitals to keep babies warm while sleeping.

Expectations for Your Doctor Visits

If your baby is breastfeeding, his doctor will probably want to see him in the office two to three days after discharge from the hospital. This visit is just to check in and make sure that he is not losing too much weight and that your milk supply is coming in. The doctor can also check for potential jaundice at this visit. If your baby is formula-fed, he will be seen in the office one or two weeks after birth. Routines may vary slightly for each provider.

Your baby's weight checks will be the main point of your visits during the first month. He will not receive any shots until his two-month visit, so rest easy.

If you have any questions or concerns, do not be afraid to discuss them with your pediatrician. It is a good idea to write down your questions throughout the weeks or months so that you remember to bring them up at baby's visit. Even though these first few visits will be pretty uneventful, baby may cry from simply having his clothes and diaper removed. It is often hard for a new mom to recall all of her once-looming questions in the midst of the visit. Bring your list and take the time to ask the doctor any questions you have. There are no stupid questions for a new mom. Your pediatrician has likely heard them all.

Common Questions You May Have This Month

I've heard that you shouldn't give your baby a pacifier or let him suck his thumb. Is this true?

Sucking is a natural way that babies soothe themselves. Additionally, the incidence of SIDS has been shown to decrease in babies who use a pacifier. In the first one to two weeks, it is best to let your baby latch on to your breast if he needs soothing. Giving a pacifier to a baby who is still learning to breastfeed can cause problems. But after a few weeks, using a binky to help calm your baby can be very effective. Hence the term "pacifier"—it is meant to pacify or soothe baby when he is upset. Babies who have a pacifier in their mouths nonstop can have some speech delay compared to their non-plugged peers. If you choose to use a pacifier, try to use it only when your baby is truly distressed or falling asleep. Pediatric dentists often feel that if you have to choose between the thumb and the pacifier, pick the pacifier. Thumb-sucking is far more harmful to the position of developing teeth than a pacifier. Either way, it's a habit you're going to want him to give up one day.

When is it okay to take my newborn out for the first time?

I always recommend that parents wait at least three or four weeks before taking their baby out into a public place for the first time. Especially for the first two weeks, both mom and baby need a chance to heal, rest, and get into the swing of things before the stress of being out and about. But after that, the decision should be based on common sense. If it's the middle of summer and you're going to a small cookout with friends, it's probably okay to show off your new bundle of joy. If it's January, in the peak of flu season and you're thinking of taking the baby with you to visit a friend in the hospital, that's probably not a good idea. You have the right to say no to anyone who appears ill and wants to hold or touch your baby. Make people (everyone, including Grandma and Uncle Bob) wash their hands or use hand sanitizer before holding the baby. The promise of "It's okay, my hands are clean" is not good enough. If there is a three-year-old whose nose is pouring snot begging to kiss your baby, and her mom says "Oh, she just has allergies," politely decline and let the child blow kisses from across the room.

My baby seems to spit up a lot. Is this normal?

Spitting up is a common problem for newborns. Most babies should be expected to have some spit-up from time to time. There are easy precautions that parents can take to reduce spit-up. First, burp your baby frequently during feedings, every five to ten minutes if breastfeeding and every 1 to 2 ounces if bottle-feeding. Effective burping may prevent spitting up. Next, keep your infant's head positioned higher than his trunk while feeding, and keep him upright for twenty to thirty minutes after feedings. You may need to give less volume of liquid at each feeding and feed him more frequently. If you are formula-feeding, you may feel the urge to change formulas to alleviate these symptoms. It is always best to discuss changing formulas with your pediatrician prior to doing so, as frequent changes may be upsetting to baby's tummy.

As long as your baby continues to gain weight and does not seem to be in any pain, spitting up is more of a nuisance than a medical concern.

Mommy Care

The first few weeks postpartum are some of the most beautiful and most challenging times in your life. As you embrace your new role of motherhood, it's helpful to know what changes to expect in your body as you recover from the process of birthing.

It takes around two weeks for your body to get accustomed to not being pregnant anymore. Your circulatory system increased by 150 percent in the pregnant state. The uterus required this extra blood and fluid to nurture your baby. Within minutes of birth, the uterine muscle clamps down, and the blood supply to the uterus decreases. You lose some of the excess pregnancy blood at delivery, but the rest of the fluid has to be filtered out (that's a nice way to say you pee a lot) over the next two weeks. During this time, you may experience some intermittent swelling as your body figures out what to do with all the extra fluid, since your uterus no longer needs it. The swelling can be significant, but as long as it is symmetric (i.e., both legs are equally swollen and not just one) and your blood pressure is normal, then it is considered normal.

It also takes about two weeks for the hormones of pregnancy to get out of your system. Add wacky hormones, sleep deprivation, and the entire experience of having a baby together, and you get an emotional roller coaster. With time and sleep, you do begin to feel more like yourself by the two-week mark. If at two weeks you still have crying spells or are feeling sad and empty inside, this may be a sign of postpartum depression, and you should contact your doctor.

The uterus grows to over a hundred times its normal size and must shrink back to normal over the next six weeks. The uterus is a muscle, so it has to contract to shrink. Most women feel this as a cramping sensation. With each delivery, you may notice the cramping after delivery getting worse, especially with nursing. This is normal and tends to improve by postpartum day three.

For moms who deliver vaginally, recovery will be dependent on the extent of vaginal tearing that occurred with delivery. Women who are blessed with no tears will likely experience some pressure and aching in their bottom, but this will usually resolve within the week. Those with episiotomies and minor tears will need two to three weeks to heal. Doctors currently use stitches that dissolve. Ice for twenty-four hours and then moist heat, such as a warm bath, for the next week can help soothe the discomfort.

Constipation is common postpartum, and using a stool softener (docusate sodium) can be helpful. Also drinking plenty of water, especially if you are breast-feeding, is a must. Having to strain for a bowel movement can cause pulling on your vaginal stitches, which is painful.

For the less than 2 percent of women who experience significant vaginal tearing that extends into their rectum, recovery will likely be closer to a month. They will be given specific instructions to care for their incisions and will need to stay on the stool softener for an extended amount of time.

Cesarean section recovery is often dependent on the type of delivery. Women who labor for two days, push for three hours, and then get a cesarean section—in addition to deserving really awesome mother's day gifts for the rest of their lives—are going to have a much tougher recovery than moms who arrive well rested for an elective cesarean for breech presentation. This is due to the strain on the body from traditional labor prior to the cesarean section delivery.

For the first two weeks after a cesarean section, you should limit your lifting to less than 20 pounds and focus only on caring for yourself and the baby. After two weeks, you can slowly increase activity, with driving and gentle walks. Full exercise should be delayed until after your six-week postpartum visit.

The incision itself should be kept clean and dry. When showering, squeeze a small amount of soapy water over the wound and let the water rinse it off.

If your incision was closed with dissolvable sutures, these will often dissolve about five weeks after delivery. At times, the edges of the incision will open slightly, about the size of a pea, and form a scab. This is normal, as long as there is no redness or purulent drainage.

Constipation, while often discussed as part of a vaginal delivery, can actually be one of the most painful symptoms following a cesarean section. During the surgery, your bowels get exposed to air and often get touched by surgical sponges. As a result the bowels take a few days to "wake up" and return to normal function. Usually, it takes 24 to 48 hours for you to pass gas. Commonly used medications such as narcotic pain pills and anti-nausea meds can further slow bowel function. Breastfeeding may also add to constipation.

With all these factors in play, it's good to plan ahead to keep constipation under control. Often, if you wait until the symptoms occur, you find yourself fighting an uphill and painful battle. Hydration is key. Drinking 80–100 ounces of water a day is recommended. Additionally it may be helpful to take Colace (100 mg) twice a day until regular bowel movements are established. Try eating high fiber food such as prunes, melons, and vegetables or taking a fiber supplement. If you have not had a bowel movement within four days of delivery, you can take milk of magnesia to help stimulate bowel function. You can repeat the milk of magnesia dose daily if other strategies aren't working to produce regular, soft stools. Continue these strategies for at least two weeks after surgery. Some women will need to continue the stool softeners for the entire time they are breastfeeding.

Even several months after a cesarean section, it is normal to have some pulling sensations in your lower abdomen when you twist or move quickly. These are usually sharp, brief pains due to scar tissue formation in the suture knots in your abdominal wall. These pains are often to the side of your actual incision. This is because the internal incisions of a cesarean section are much larger than the skin incision.

Up to 70 percent of women who have a vaginal delivery will experience some leaking of urine when they cough or sneeze. The bladder is supported by the pelvic floor muscles, which get stretched significantly with delivery. The majority of women return to normal by six months postpartum, with the help of Kegel exercises. If at six months you still experience leaking, then check with your doctor.

Kegel Exercises

Kegel exercises help strengthen the muscles that control your bowel and bladder functions. You don't want to tighten your abdominal muscles or thigh muscles. To make sure you are using the right muscles, it is best initially to do these exercises while you are peeing. Begin to pee, then contract your muscles to make the stream stop. Hold the muscles tight for ten seconds, then release. Repeat ten times. Once you have learned the correct muscles to use, you can do Kegels anywhere. Do three sets of ten to start.

Each mother's recovery from delivery will be as different as the women and deliveries themselves. Some bounce back in days; others take months to really feel back to themselves. As you recover, listen to your body. Aches, cramps, and brief, sharp pains are expected and slowly improve with time. Severe and persistent pain or fever should be evaluated by your doctor.

A Real-Life Story

Breastfeeding

Stephanie Gill, mom to James Macklin

I have always prided myself on being able to push through tough situations with two mantras: "No pain, no gain" and "I can do all things through him who gives me strength." Nothing, however, prepared me for the *pain* I was destined to endure with breastfeeding. This experience redefined how much I was willing to give in order to achieve something I felt convicted to do.

Within hours of giving birth, my husband and I were actively working to teach James Macklin to establish a frequent feeding routine. Despite feeling numb with the pain medication for the C-section, I noticed immediately that James Macklin's latch didn't feel quite right. I was told that discomfort is normal, but it dissipates as the nipples become desensitized.

By the time I left the hospital, my abdomen felt as though I had never been pregnant and had a major surgery; my nipples were another story. I was in excruciating pain. I tried applying ample nipple cream after each feeding, expressing milk to prevent engorgement, and using a nipple guard, all in vain. When James Macklin was nursing, I would grit my teeth, and often I would cry until he was through. The pain continued when he wasn't nursing, which made me irritable and depressed. I was miserable, deflated, and wondering why other moms could handle this without batting an eye.

After three weeks of this kind of torture, I finally gave in and reached out to a lactation consultant, who concluded that James Macklin was a *chewer*. She explained that he wasn't just biting when he latched on but that he was chewing as he fed. Despite the sixty-five-dollar prescription cream, the pain continued for months, and I was unsure how I would reach my goal of breastfeeding for another day, much less for a full year.

Desperately, I sent an email to my friends, detailing my struggles with breastfeeding and how I had never imagined it would be as difficult as I was finding it to be. I asked for prayers and any advice that my friends could offer, because I so badly wanted to be able to breastfeed my child. Well, God heard those prayers, and one friend gave me a pointer that became the inflection point that almost never was. She showed me a trick to foster a good latch, and with that I began to comfortably nurse my child as though I had never had any trouble.

I now have one month until I have reached my breastfeeding goal. Every day, I look at his precious face and thank God for reminding me that anything worth having is worth working for. My mantras still resonate in my heart, but with more passion than they ever possessed. I encourage other new mothers to work through the pain and not to be too quick to give up; the solution may come in an email behind a prayer, but we *can* do all things through him.

Truth for the Journey

"Trust in the Lord with all your heart and lean not on your own understanding;
in all your ways acknowledge him, and he will direct your paths."
Proverbs 3:5–6

With a host of available resources from books to websites to smartphone apps, we are not at a loss for information about how to take care of a baby. If there were a modern-day version of this passage, I think it would read, ". . . and lean not on your own understanding or that of the countless voices you read on various blogs, Facebook pages, and Twitter feeds." The very first truth we hope you'll come to understand on this journey—the very foundation of wisdom that you will need to mother this life that has been entrusted to you—is that you cannot lean on your own understanding. Our minds could never comprehend the complexity of a new baby adjusting to life outside of the womb. It's one of the marvelous mysteries of creation. When we focus only on our own understanding or on the many voices that we come across each day, we will experience confusion. Therefore we are left, in a state of desperation, to cling to the Lord, acknowledging him and thus allowing him to direct our path.

As Dr. Johnston discussed in this chapter, there are a wide variety of details and decisions that you will encounter during the first few weeks of baby's life. Choices will continue to present themselves to you in the months ahead and for the rest of your child's life, so understanding this truth now will empower you for the future. When we acknowledge the Lord and let him direct our paths, we are placing our trust in him—in his capable hands, in his character, in his love for us. When we surrender to him in this way, we can then begin to trust ourselves and our instincts because we know they are God-given. This is Holy Spirit leading, and it is available to lead you through each day.

Let's get one thing straight before we go any further. There is no such thing as the perfect mom. There, I said it. If you've got your heart set on being supermom, then you might as well give up now. It's not possible, and anyone who allows you to think otherwise is flat-out lying. But let's face it—it's not usually other people who impose the goal of supermom on us. We do that to ourselves. Your quest for this unachievable honor may be subtle. It may even be subconscious. If you come to terms right now with your humanity, you will do much better as you walk out your days as a mom. All you can do is your best, and covered by his grace, that will be just perfect for your little one.

A Beautiful Bond

I don't think there is anything more beautiful than the immediate bond between a mother and child. Whether you labored for days, delivered via cesarean section, or were united with your baby through the miracle of adoption, you were destined to be this child's mommy before he was ever conceived.. The Lord knew you would come to this place, holding new life in your arms, marveling at the wonder of it all. He's prepared your heart to open wide to this little person. This bond is his gift to you. No matter what happens in the months to come, no matter what trials and adjustments you will face, one thing will remain—the connection you feel to this life. I believe this phenomenon is a large part of how we make it through the initial crazy, sleepless, confusing days of new motherhood. Keep in mind, though, that the bond you feel with your baby may be very different than the bond of another mother and child. Your connection to your baby will be just as different as your personality and his, compared to another. Focus your thoughts on the bond that is growing within your arms without looking outward to what others may be experiencing. This is perhaps your first practice in not comparing yourself to other moms.

Besides the natural bond you feel with your baby, there are many activities that can help you grow even closer to him in the early days. Some of the sweetest ways to bond with your baby are by singing and talking to him. This is very soothing to your baby because he was surrounded by the rhythms of your voice for nine months. It's so familiar and comforting. As you hold him in your arms, let go of any inhibitions and simply share your heart openly through affirming words and sweet songs.

After I had my first child, I started a routine of reading the Bible to her during her morning feeding. It allowed me to take ten minutes to start the day off in the

Word myself while speaking words of truth over her. Of course, she didn't understand what I was reading, but I believe the Word to be powerful and life-giving, so I knew speaking it to her was very positive. Whether you choose to read the Word or classic children's books, reading to your child and allowing him the comfort of hearing your familiar voice is a wonderful way to bond.

There are many mainstream parenting books that discourage rocking your baby to sleep for fear it will cause him to become dependent on the ritual to settle down. No matter what your personal viewpoint is on the subject, I encourage you to spend time rocking your little one. No one ever screwed up a baby by cuddling him close and rocking him to sleep. Sure, you may want to avoid making it a habit because, depending on the child, it could interfere with his ability to fall asleep on his own (more on this later), but do not deprive yourself and your child of the privilege of such sweet moments.

Babywearing

Another great way to bond with your baby is by wearing him. There are many options currently on the market for baby carriers, and you can find our readers' favorites in the Appendix at the end of this book. Babywearing is a wonderfully practical way for a mom to keep baby close as he adjusts to life outside the womb. Your baby will love the feeling of being snuggled into your chest, hearing your heart beat like he did constantly for nine months. Besides the satisfying feeling of holding baby close, you'll also appreciate having two free hands while carrying baby. So babywearing is a win-win! It may take a while for you to get used to a baby carrier, and you may need to try a few out to find the best fit. Ask around to your other mommy friends about which carrier they prefer. They may have one you can borrow.

Seek Wisdom

One of the verses I shared with moms-to-be at the end of *The Pregnancy Companion* is found in Proverbs 4. In the chapter appropriately titled, in many translations, "Wisdom Is Supreme," King Solomon implores readers in verse 7: "Wisdom is the principal thing; therefore get wisdom. And in all your getting, get understanding" (NKJV). I just love the wording here. "In all your getting, get understanding." As if to say, "Hey, while you are at Babies R Us, stocking the nursery with bedding and blankets and burp cloths, make sure you pick up some wisdom so you can care for your little one, too. Okay?"

From the moment you lay eyes on your precious miracle, you will try to understand every sound, gesture, and cry that comes from him. But you simply can't know exactly what is going on in that tiny, little head . . . much less his heart. In actuality, your baby doesn't even truly understand what is going on. It's all so new to him. There is no possible way for you to perfectly interpret every cue. The only chance you have of getting it right is to diligently seek wisdom. When you look to the Lord for wisdom, he'll give it generously (James 1:5) and accurately—wisdom that is meant for you and your family. Let the Holy Spirit be your guide, and you will experience peace in the midst of these early days of motherhood.

Pick your battles. We are going to discuss many issues in this book that you will encounter throughout your baby's first year. From breastfeeding to vaccinations to sleep scheduling, there are many topics on which you will seek wisdom. First and foremost, though, you need to pick your battles. What do you need to fight for? Is it breastfeeding? Then put your whole heart and mind into contending for your ability to breastfeed your baby. For many moms, the battle may present itself. You may not be given the luxury of choosing. Whatever issue presents itself to you or you choose to fight for, focus in and avoid the trap of making every topic of utmost importance. This is the beginning of the wisdom you should seek from God. What is he calling you to focus on? Where does he want to do a work of growth in your life as he stretches you as a mom? I don't believe he'd overwhelm you with too many issues to deal with at once. Ask him to open your eyes and then choose. Do not allow yourself to be buried under a mountain of worry. You'll miss out on so much joy under there.

Beware of the Internet. I can promise you that two things are true of Internet searches. 1) You can *always* find someone who agrees with what you are already thinking. 2) You can *always* find someone who disagrees with what you are already thinking. So what then are you left with after you frantically type your question into Google and hit *enter*? Confusion. I'm not saying you should never Google any of your questions. You simply need to guard yourself against believing whatever you read. I have a friend who always says, "You can't Google wisdom." This is so true. While you can Google knowledge and information, your search will never produce results that offer perfect, God-given wisdom for your unique situation. There are many resources on the web for solid, medical, and practical advice. You must sift through the information, however, and ask God for wisdom in interpreting what you read and discerning what is best for *your* baby. Search for knowledge but pray for wisdom. I caution you, also, to never let the Internet take the place of your doctor's advice.

*If you are able to trust what you read on a random website or forum before the advice of your pediatrician, then you have trust issues with your baby's doctor, and you should address those issues immediately.

Use parenting (method) books with caution. As I said in the Introduction, it's not that I think parenting books are all bad. I just know that they've caused a lot of unnecessary stress and fear in new moms due to the way they present their advice. For a "method" book to become a best seller, the author must present the information as fact—as the be-all and end-all solution to your problem. But you and I both know that parenting is not one size fits all. There are many variables that must be considered when deciding what course of action to take with your child. Since there is no way these authors could possibly know every detail of your specific situation, they could not have written the book with you in mind. That is why we encourage you to seek the Lord first for his leading. You may glean helpful nuggets of truth from these books, but you cannot believe them to contain absolute truth for you or your child. Read the books that seem to resonate with your personal philosophies on parenting, and then bathe that information in prayer and constant discussion with your spouse or support system. Most importantly, *do not* let yourself feel like a failure if a method does not work for your baby.

Tracking Baby's Schedule

Although your baby will not be on any type of "schedule" for a few months, you may elect to keep track of his feeding and sleeping patterns as you learn his tendencies. If for no other reason, you may choose to track your baby's schedule so you can remember the last time you fed him. Don't underestimate the effects of sleep deprivation. There were times I couldn't remember when I had changed my baby's diaper or went potty myself in those first few weeks. There are a few wonderful resources available for keeping track of baby's patterns, including journals, smartphone apps, and websites. We've listed our favorites as well as given you a schedule template in the Appendix at the end of this book.

Grace for Lack of Sleep

One of the toughest adjustments for new moms is lack of sleep. You will be encouraged to "sleep when the baby sleeps," which is good advice; however, it's not always that simple. If you have another child in your home, it may be impossible to sleep when the new baby sleeps. As you move throughout your days and settle in a bit, you will find strategies for getting as much sleep as possible. In the meantime, pray daily for his grace to cover you. Second Corinthians 12:9 says, "My grace is sufficient for you, for my power is made perfect in weakness." I can't think of a greater weakness than pure exhaustion. Acknowledge your lack, and he will come and allow his power to rest upon you.

Before we wrap up this first chapter, I want to encourage you to ask those around you for help. Do not feel like you have to do this new mother thing alone. Don't try to prove that you can. You might be able to, but someone will suffer at your attempt. First and foremost, ask your spouse for help. Hopefully he is more than willing to lend a hand, but in the event that he is a bit clueless, communicate openly and clearly what you need. If you are a single mom, lean into your family for support. Next, gather friends and even extended family members to share in the joy and the responsibility that come with a new baby. Let them know you would appreciate meals, house cleaning, help with laundry. Don't ignore their offer to help. Graciously accept all the help you can get. If no one offers, I'd like to tell you to get a new family, but it's probably too late for that, so suck it up and ask them to help you. Beg if you have to. Finally, if you attend a particular church regularly, seek out the people who handle congregational care. Hopefully they are used to providing meals and other assistance to new moms. Whatever you can do to assemble help, do it. After all, they say it takes a village. . . .

Prayer Concerns

Baby's adjustment

Mommy's adjustment

Lack of sleep

Healing for mommy

Breastfeeding

A Prayer for Your Journey

Dear Lord,

Thank you for the precious gift of life I hold in my arms. What an amazing picture of your goodness and love. I ask you to give me wisdom for each day. Help me to seek you first, relying on your faithful Holy Spirit to answer every question on my mother heart. I ask for peace to cover us, even in the midst of this major life adjustment. No matter how this baby rocks my world, I pray that I would daily be reminded that this is an amazing miracle I am so privileged to steward. I trust you, Lord, to provide everything we need to flourish as mother and child. Thank you for your faithful guidance. Amen.

Write a prayer here for your own personal journey.

Journal

Record your thoughts, questions, and baby's milestones here.

Settling In

Baby Stats

Babies will gain an average of 1½ to 2 pounds per month during the first few months and grow in length approximately 1 inch per month. By two months, babies range from 7 pounds, 8 ounces to 12 pounds, 5 ounces (3.4–5.6 kg) in weight and 20 to 23 inches (51–58 cm) in length.

At each well-child visit, your doctor will weigh your baby and measure his length and head circumference. She might show you a growth chart in the office and discuss your baby's percentiles. These percentiles show you exactly how your baby compares to other children the same age. The fiftieth percentile is exactly average. While doctors do look at the numbers for that particular day, the more important reason to plot babies' measurements is to make sure their growth is trending at a predictable rate. The percentiles that a baby measures during his first year of life may not be predictive of how large or small he will be as an adult. Interruptions in an otherwise steady growth chart can alert your doctor to potential medical or developmental concerns.

Development Checker at Two Months

Typical Skills

- ❑ Social smiles, gurgles, and coos
- ❑ Holds head up consistently
- ❑ Follows movement across a field of vision

Concerning Signs

- ❑ No response to loud sounds
- ❑ Lack of movement in arms and legs

Language

Smiles and more smiles! Newborns are very sweet and cuddly, but let's face it—they don't give much feedback except when they are upset. Finally, at about six to eight weeks old, your baby will begin to sport a social smile. Nothing will delight him more than hearing you talk to him in a sweet, soothing voice. He will be able to watch faces and may start to track you as you walk across the room. He may even begin to coo and babble. Talking and singing to your baby now will help develop his early language and social skills.

Movement

Head support. You may notice now that baby will start to lift his head up off the floor or up from your shoulder when you are holding him. He is working on his coordination and strengthening his muscles. Baby will still need help from you, though, since his head can suddenly jerk back or forward at this age. He will not develop the ability to hold his own head well until about three months of age.

Movement of arms and legs. For the first month or so of life, babies tend to stay in their fetal position and prefer to have their arms and legs tucked in just as they were in the womb. Most babies like to be swaddled in the first weeks of life for exactly this reason. Between one and two months of age, you may find that baby likes to stretch out a little more. He will stretch his arms and legs out and maybe even start to kick a little. Baby's movements at this age will not be for any real purpose except to stretch. It will be another few months before baby will actually reach out for something he wants. You should expect baby to move both arms and legs equally. If you find that baby always stretches out one arm and not the other, it can be a sign that he has an injury or other congenital problem, and his doctor should be alerted right away. The same holds true for baby's legs. If he stretches out and kicks one leg but keeps the other constantly flexed or bent, it can be a sign of a hip problem, and his doctor should take a look.

Baby Care
Feeding

By four weeks of age, most moms find a good breastfeeding routine. Your milk supply is well established, and both you and your baby have figured things out. A breastfed baby may still want to nurse for fifteen to thirty minutes every two to three hours, but he should have longer stretches of sleep at night. He may still want to cluster feed at this age as well. Many babies are ready to be on a schedule by two months of age. Schedules will be discussed further in Month Three. Babies who are exclusively breastfed should receive vitamin D supplements daily to prevent vitamin D deficiency.

Cluster Feeding

Sometimes moms are concerned when their newborn wants to breastfeed more often than every two hours. While this can be a sign that your milk supply is low, it can also be normal cluster feeding. Cluster feeding occurs when newborns eat more often than every two hours for several feedings in a row, then space other feedings out the rest of the day. Babies who cluster feed may want to eat every thirty to ninety minutes for several hours straight. This often occurs at night. It is important not to make your baby wait for a feeding during these first months. Babies are very good at regulating themselves. If he is rooting, chewing on his hands, and squirming, he is probably hungry, and you should offer him another feeding.

Formula-fed babies should be taking approximately 3 to 4 ounces of formula per feeding (every three to four hours) at one month of age and about 5 to 6 ounces per feeding at two months of age. Formula-fed babies may go a little longer between feedings, up to four hours. Signs of hunger include smacking the lips and putting hands to mouth. If your baby starts to turn his head to the bottle or pull away, he may be full. Avoid forcing him to finish the bottle if he shows signs he is full. Overfeeding is a common problem and can lead to an increase in spitting up, constipation, and rapid weight gain. Many parents are told to add rice cereal to bottles with the promise that it will help their baby "sleep through the night." It is best to avoid this temptation for several reasons. For starters, it often doesn't work.

Second, adding cereal to bottles can lead to constipation, making your baby irritable and uncomfortable rather than sleepy. Last, and most importantly, recent studies have shown a direct link between giving children solids prior to four months of age and childhood obesity.

("Starting Solids Too Early May Increase Obesity Risk," AAP, February 7, 2011, www.aap.org.)

Sleep and Schedules

There are many "method" books available that promise to help your baby fall into a good feeding and sleeping routine. For some moms, these books are miraculous and bring much-needed structure to their lives. Talk to friends and do some reading and see if any of these "methods" fit your style. I agree with most methods that consistency is the key. Pick the plan that sounds good to you, then stick with it (for at least a few weeks). No baby is going to follow the plan at first. Your baby didn't read the book, so you have to give the technique a little time. And no matter how perfectly you follow the method, there will be good days and bad days. By the two-month mark, your baby should be able to make it through the night with only one or two feedings. For example, a typical schedule might include a bedtime feeding around eight or nine, followed by a 2:00 A.M. feeding, then a 5:00 or 6:00 A.M. feeding.

Breastfed babies will continue to eat every two to three hours during the day but may stretch to every four hours at night. Formula-fed babies can typically go a little longer between feedings—every three to four hours during the day with only one feeding overnight.

Diapering

Diaper rash. Diaper rashes are quite common in newborns. To prevent diaper rash from occurring, you may want to apply a thin layer of petroleum jelly (Vaseline, A&D ointment) over baby's diaper area with every change. Frequent diaper changes will also help prevent diaper rash from forming. You might notice that your baby has a reaction to certain brands of diapers, wipes, or laundry detergents if using cloth diapers. If you notice a diaper rash, consider what new products you might have used on his skin or in washing his diapers that could have caused the reaction. Yeast diaper rashes are also common in newborns. A yeast rash will often look like bright red, shiny patches of skin with surrounding little bright red dots ("satellite" lesions). Relieve diaper rash by applying an over the counter zinc oxide cream (Desitin, Boudreaux's). If baby's rash persists, ask his doctor about stronger diaper cream options available through your pharmacy. Yeast rashes are best treated with antifungal medications such as Monistat or Lotrimin twice a day. If your baby has a diaper rash that is not improving despite all your efforts, he should be seen by his pediatrician.

Stools. There is no right answer to how much your baby should poop each day. Every baby is different. Stools can look like thin mustard or be more formed. Your baby may have a bowel movement six times a day or only once every two to three days. If your baby is crying in pain or his stomach appears more round than usual, he may be constipated. If you are concerned your baby is having too frequent stools or not enough, you should consult your pediatrician.

Bathing

Now that your baby's umbilical stump has detached, he is ready for a real bath. Most parents find it easiest to bathe newborns in a small basin or sink lined with a soft, clean towel. Run the water a few inches deep and test the temperature to make sure it is not too hot. Gather everything you will need for the bath including shampoo, body wash, a cup for rinsing his hair, a washcloth, and a clean, dry towel. You may also want to bring the phone or anything else you may need close to the area where you will bathe your baby. Remember, once he is in the water, you will have to take him back out and with you if you have forgotten anything. Never leave your baby unattended in a bath, even for a few seconds.

To place him in the bath, support his head with one hand and then guide his body into the bath with your other hand. Your baby's first baths should be kept very brief. He may protest a little at first. If he gets very upset, you may want to return to doing sponge baths for a few weeks and then try a real bath again. Bath toys are not needed at this age and should be saved for when baby is older. Eventually, he will be eager for bath time and a chance to splash and play! Most parents bathe their babies every other day, or at least twice a week.

Hair Loss. If your baby was born with a significant amount of hair, you may begin to notice some bald patches on his head. Infants typically lose hair in the first six months of life due to pure friction. As baby sleeps or sits for an extended period of time, his head rubs on the mattress or car seat. Hair loss is perfectly normal and new follicle growth will occur. Do not be alarmed if you see these bald patches. They are particularly evident in babies born with a lot of dark hair. Soon enough, your baby's hair will begin to grow and strengthen in the follicle. If you notice him balding on a particular side of the head, pay close attention to the way he sleeps and sits. Adjusting his position may help prevent or delay his hair loss—or at the very least, even it out.

Baby Safety

Environment. Make sure that your home is a safe environment for your child. Set water heaters to a maximum temperature of 120°F to prevent scalding injuries in the bath. Make every provision for your home to be a drug-free and tobacco-free environment for your baby. Provide direct adult supervision of your child at all times. Do not rely on older children to watch a newborn for you. Make sure your home (including your baby's nursery) is equipped with smoke detectors and change the batteries regularly. Know the number for poison control and keep it in an easy-to-find place such as the refrigerator door. Be careful with hot liquids such as coffee or tea around your baby.

Outdoors. Sun exposure should be avoided altogether for infants less than six months of age. If you absolutely must take baby out in the sun, keep him in the shade as much as possible. Although sunscreen labels often say their product is not for use on babies under six months, this is primarily because the AAP has recommended complete sun avoidance prior to six months and not because the product is actually harmful. If you must have baby outdoors, you may apply sunscreen to any exposed areas of skin, such as the face and the tops of baby's hands. Make sure he wears a hat with a wide brim to protect his head, face, ears, and neck. Choose a sunscreen that says "broad spectrum" and protects against UVA and UVB rays. The higher a sunscreen's SPF (sun protection factor), the better the coverage against UV rays. You should always choose a sunscreen of at least SPF 30. Sunscreen should be applied twenty to thirty minutes prior to going outdoors in order to be most beneficial. Reapply sunscreen every two hours, as it will wear off from soaking into the skin. Avoid peak hours of sunlight exposure from 10:00 A.M. to 4:00 P.M. whenever possible. Even on a cloudy day, it is possible to get a sunburn. Make a habit of applying sunscreen anytime you will be outdoors. Set a good example right from the start, and don't forget to apply it on your own skin as well.

Expectations for Your Doctor Visits

A "well visit" is when your baby is healthy and seen regularly by the doctor to check his growth and development. Well visits after the first month typically occur when baby is two months, four months, six months, nine months, and twelve months old. A "sick visit" is when you see the doctor for any acute illnesses or ongoing issues of concern that you have (such as chronic constipation or reflux). A well visit may not be the best time to tell your doctor about four or five issues that have been going on for weeks or months. Of course, you can always bring issues of concern to your baby's doctor, and questions are welcome and expected. But don't let too many key issues pile up for a well visit. Make an appointment in between well checks to discuss any major concerns. Or, if you're unable to make a separate appointment, tell the office staff when you make the appointment that you have an extensive list of concerns. That way, extra time can be blocked for your child.

For many parents, the most anticipated part of the two-month checkup is vaccines. According to CDC and AAP recommendations, your baby is scheduled to receive several vaccines at his two-month visit. Your child's doctor will review each vaccine with you at his appointment and answer any questions that you may have. If you have concerns, talk with your child's pediatrician and do not be afraid to ask specific questions.

I have no doubt vaccinations will be the most controversial issue in this book. I struggled as I thought about what to say and how it might affect new moms. I want *all* new moms to feel they are being supported and uplifted in this book. New parents just want to do what they feel is best for their baby. Every decision is a struggle, and the topic of immunizations can be a tense one. No matter what your position is regarding vaccines, I hope that you will find support and encouragement along your journey.

As a mom, I'll admit—when my son had his two-month checkup and received his first set of shots, I was a little nervous. Not because I was concerned about the safety of the vaccines, but because it's hard to see your child cry. I worried that he might be in pain later that night or that he would get a fever with the vaccines. Although some local tenderness and mild fevers are possible, these are usually very mild or even nonexistent. As it turned out, he barely even flinched when he received his vaccines. He was such a trooper. He had no fevers and no marks on his legs. Most importantly, I had peace of mind that I was doing everything in my power to keep him healthy.

The decision to vaccinate or not vaccinate is an extremely touchy subject for many. Those who feel very strongly one way or the other tend to be very vocal and even confrontational to others about their beliefs. Some people will argue that vaccines aren't safe or that their child is getting too many at once. Others feel that by not vaccinating, you are being irresponsible as a parent and not protecting your child properly from preventable illnesses. Many new parents are left feeling afraid and confused, and the number one place they will turn to for answers is the Internet. Although there is some very good information about vaccines on the Internet, there is false and unscientific information as well. Be careful what you read, and make sure that you choose reliable sources when researching questions.

I feel morally and medically obligated to state clearly that I believe one hundred percent in vaccines. I vaccinated my son completely and kept him on schedule. I would urge you to consider vaccinating your child. Decide if the recommended vaccine schedule is right for your family. Just because family members or other moms at your church only give their child one vaccine at a time doesn't mean you have to do that. Speak in advance with your child's pediatrician if you are considering an alternate vaccine schedule. Although alternate vaccine schedules are better than no schedule at all, some doctors do not support alternate schedules and may ask you to choose a doctor more in line with your beliefs.

Even if you have decided not to vaccinate at all, your child still needs to go in for all of his well-child checkups. These visits are about much more than a set of shots. Your baby's doctor will want to track his growth and development with you and discuss any concerns that you may have.

If you have decided to vaccinate your child, the following is a list of vaccines that you should expect at your baby's two-month visit. Some of these vaccines are given separately, and some may be combined into a single injection, depending on what your doctor carries in her office. This discussion of vaccines is not meant to scare new parents, but rather to educate you on the medical reasons behind why these vaccines are recommended by physicians and the AAP. Pediatricians are devoted to making sure children grow up as safe and healthy as possible. The information comes from the following websites, which are the most credible resources for up-to-date information about vaccines: www.cdc.gov, www.immunize.org , and www.healthychildren.org.

Rotavirus. Rotavirus is a common cause of vomiting and diarrhea in infants. It is a particularly severe form of the "stomach bug," and prior to the vaccine, it hospitalized tens of thousands of babies every year. In developing countries, rotavirus remains a major cause of infant mortality due to severe dehydration leading to death. It is a liquid vaccine that your child will drink. This vaccine is a series of three doses given at two, four, and six months of age.

Pneumococcal. There are more than ninety types of *Streptococcus pneumoniae* bacteria. The pneumococcal vaccine protects against the thirteen most common forms of the disease. Pneumococcus is a deadly form of meningitis, killing one in ten children infected. Although meningitis is certainly the most severe complication of pneumococcus, this bacteria was also a major cause of ear infections and blood infections prior to development of the vaccine. It is a series of four vaccines given at two, four, six, and twelve to fifteen months of age.

Hepatitis B. Hepatitis B is a virus that infects both children and adults. It is spread via blood and other body fluids. Mothers who have hepatitis B can pass it along to their newborns. Hepatitis B can be spread via contact with blood or body fluids through open sores, bites, and cuts. It can also spread through contaminated needle sticks and sexual contact. Hepatitis B is a series of three vaccines. The first dose is often given prior to discharge from the newborn nursery at the hospital. A second dose is given at one to two months of age, and the final dose at six to eighteen months of age.

DTaP. This is a combination vaccine that protects children against diphtheria, tetanus, and pertussis (whooping cough). Diphtheria infection causes a thick covering over the back of the throat, leading to breathing problems and heart failure. Tetanus causes severe, painful muscle contraction that prevents a victim from breathing adequately. It is deadly in two out of ten cases. Pertussis causes severe cough and respiratory distress, and in the most severe cases, pneumonia, seizures, and even death. The DTaP vaccine is a series of five vaccines given at two, four, six, fifteen to eighteen months, and four to six years of age.

Polio. Polio is caused by a virus. In the most severe cases, polio can cause severe meningitis or paralysis of the respiratory muscles, leading to death. Although no polio has been seen in the United States in over twenty years, it is still present in other parts of the world. It is a series of four injections, with doses at two, four, and sixteen to eighteen months and a booster dose at four to six years of age.

Hib. Haemophilus influenza type B (Hib) is a serious bacterial infection that usually occurs in young children prior to age five. Before the vaccine, Hib was the leading cause of meningitis in children under five years old. It was also a leading cause of pneumonia, serious joint infections, and blood infections. The vaccine is a series of three to four injections (depending on the type), most commonly given at two, four, six, and twelve to fifteen months of age.

Your child will receive another weight check at this visit. It will be fun but also a little bit sad to see your little one growing so fast. Your doctor may give you a handout explaining baby's physical and developmental milestones for this stage. She may even ask you to complete a questionnaire about baby's progress. If this brings up additional questions or concerns, do not hesitate to discuss them with your pediatrician.

Recommended Vaccination Schedule**

VACCINE	Birth	Month 1	Month 2	Month 4	Month 6	Month 12	Month 15	Month 18	Month 24	4+ Yrs
Hepatitis B (HBV)	1	2				3				
Rotavirus (RV)			1	2	3*					
Diphtheria, Tetanus and Pertussis (DTaP)			1	2	3		4			5
Haemophilus Influenzae Type B (Hib)			1	2	3	4				
Pneummococcal Conjungate (PCV)			1	2	3	4				4
Polio (IPV)			1	2	3	3				4
Influenza (Flu)					Given yearly starting at 6m w/ two doses given the 1st year					
Measels, Mumps and Rubella (MMR)						1				2
Varicella (Chicken Pox)						1				2
Hepatitis A (Hep A)						Two doses at least 6 months apart				

*Number of doses may vary depending on vaccine given. Please check with your doctor.
**Based on current AAP and CDC recommendations.

Common Questions You May Have This Month

I think my baby is constipated. How do I know for sure, and what can I do?

Constipation is a common complaint at this age. Babies' tummies are still sensitive to even minor changes at two months. Particularly in formula-fed babies, constipation is a frequent concern. Constipation means different things to different parents. All babies can grunt, strain, and turn red while passing a bowel movement. Just because a baby strains or turns red doesn't mean he is constipated. As long as your infant's stools are soft and not painful, it is okay. It is "normal" for a baby to poop only two to three times per week or as much as six or more times daily, depending on the individual child.

If your child does get constipated, discuss your concerns with his doctor. She may recommend something simple, such as a warm bath or a warm blanket held on baby's belly. She may also suggest giving a small amount of water or juice daily, or even adding corn syrup to the bottle to help soften the stool. Minor rectal stimulation with a rectal thermometer can also help. Finally, glycerin suppositories available over the counter can be used to help alleviate constipation.

My friend's baby has acid reflux and is on medication. My baby spits up all the time. Could he have reflux, too?

We talked about spit-up in Month One. Refer back to that section for information regarding normal spit-up in infants.

If your baby seems to be in pain after feeding or with spitting up, he could have significant gastroesophageal reflux (GERD). Babies with GERD will often cry out in pain, arch their backs, and stiffen their bodies in response to painful reflux (Sandifer's syndrome). If this happens to your baby, you should have him checked by his doctor. She may recommend minor reflux precautions as outlined in our discussion of spit-up in Month One. In addition, she may encourage you to try an elimination diet if you are breastfeeding or try a new formula such as a hydrolyzed or "hypoallergenic" variety if your baby is formula-fed. There are prescription medications that are safe in infants that may also be recommended. Fortunately, reflux is a condition that most babies will outgrow with time.

My baby is always fussy. Could he have colic?

Colic is defined as excessive fussiness and crying in a baby with no identifiable cause. The crying often happens at a predictable time of day, usually in the evenings. Colic normally starts by around four to six weeks of age and may persist for several months. Most babies outgrow colic by four to six months of age. Although some babies will have a true case of colic, most simply have a fussy time of day. As long as this fussy period is limited to a few hours daily, and the rest of the day he seems content, there is likely no serious medical problem. If your baby has colic, he will experience an extreme fussy period that may persist for longer than just a few hours per day. If he shows signs of colic, you should consult your doctor. She will likely want to examine the baby and make sure that there is no other cause for his fussiness.

No one knows exactly what causes colic. Many feel that it is related to an "immature" nervous system or digestion difficulty. Your baby may pass a lot of gas, stiffen his arms and legs, and cry out. There are over-the-counter herbal or "all natural" colic medications that are available to try, such as gripe water. Most of these medications are safe, and they may or may not help. Each baby with colic is different. Some colicky babies prefer to be swaddled and held closely, while others prefer swings and vibrating seats. It is okay to try a variety of techniques and see what works best for your baby.

If you are breastfeeding, colic symptoms can be a result of your baby being sensitive to something you are eating, such as dairy or wheat. Talk to your doctor and ask about a trial of eliminating certain foods from your diet. If you are giving formula, a hydrolyzed or "hypoallergenic" formula may be helpful to alleviate some symptoms. Ask your doctor about using over-the-counter simethicone drops (gas drops) on a regular basis if your baby seems to become fussy after eating. A proper dose administered with each feeding will often do wonders for a fussy baby.

Colic can be extremely frustrating for new parents and caregivers. You feel as if no matter what you do, you cannot make your baby happy. It is a very helpless feeling to have. If you find yourself feeling overly anxious or agitated during a colicky period, have a trusted caregiver come to your home and give you a break. Get out of the house for a walk, and take time to clear your mind. If you feel that you are becoming depressed or angry about your baby's behavior, please discuss this openly with your doctor for options that may help. No matter what, never allow yourself to lose your temper and shake your baby in frustration. As we discussed in Month One, shaking a baby can cause blindness, severe brain damage, and death.

Mommy Care

Your postpartum visit is usually scheduled for six weeks after delivery. At this visit, your doctor will perform a pelvic exam. She will make sure that your uterus has returned to normal size and that everything has healed properly from your delivery. Most moms' bleeding will have subsided by their six-week visit; occasionally, women will still be spotting or continue to have a clear yellow discharge from healing for up to eight weeks. Your doctor will screen for depression and perhaps discuss birth control options.

Sex after baby. You should refrain from having sex until after your six-week postpartum visit, where you should be given the go-ahead by your doctor. Refer to Month Four for an extensive discussion on sex after baby.

Losing the Baby Weight

During the first few weeks of baby's life, he requires your almost constant attention. This is a stage that is about survival. "Taking care of yourself" during the first few weeks amounts to making sure you get a little sleep and maybe a shower. As you begin to develop a routine with your baby, establishing healthy habits for yourself becomes more feasible. The key is to have patience and realistic expectations and to allow yourself some grace on the days when you are a sleep-deprived mess.

When you look at the scale at your six-week appointment, all the water weight is gone. If you weigh more than you did before conception at this point, what's left is the "baby weight." Don't be discouraged by the numbers, and don't be in a hurry to get your waist back. This is a time to get healthy, not crash diet or deprive yourself. Your body needs energy in a way that it's never needed it before, so an overly restrictive diet is going to make you miserable and set you up to fail.

Some women find themselves back to their pre-pregnancy weight already at this point, which is great. Others may find that their weight is in an unhealthy range, and for them it may be time to work on healthier habits. Those sweet little ladies at church have likely stopped bringing you yummy, cheesy, carb-loaded casseroles, and your baby is sleeping (at least a little), so now you can focus more on yourself.

For most women, getting back to basic healthy nutritional choices may be all they need. Instead of depriving yourself and counting calories, begin by making smart choices. You will feel better and may be back in your pre-baby jeans before you know it.

Healthy Diet Tips:

- Consume at least three servings of vegetables and two servings of fruit per day.
- Eat lean protein with each meal (chicken, fish, sirloin, beans).
- Drink 80–100 ounces of water per day.
- Cut out sugary drinks. Sodas and juices are empty calories.
- Avoid all fried foods and fast food.
- Be wary of "healthy" processed food like diet cookies and chips. These are empty calories with poor nutritional value.
- Focus on hearty, quick snacks that give you nutrition and energy: nuts, veggies, and hummus; bananas, berries, yogurt, trail mix, and whole grain breads are all good choices.

There is no magic formula to get the baby weight off fast. Actually, losing weight too fast can affect your milk supply. Now is the time to establish healthy eating habits and get moving.

Continuing a multivitamin during your first year postpartum is recommended and essential if you are breastfeeding. Getting the recommended 1000 mg a day of calcium from your diet can be challenging, so an additional calcium supplement may also be necessary. If you are counting calories, you should add 600 calories a day if breastfeeding.

Exercise. Moms who have a vaginal delivery can typically resume exercise at one month postpartum, while women with cesarean section deliveries usually need to wait six to eight weeks. Aim for at least thirty minutes of exercise five days a week. Refer to Month Seven for more tips on exercise after baby.

Truth for the Journey

"But the wisdom that comes from heaven is first of all pure; then peace-loving, considerate, submissive, full of mercy and good fruit, impartial and sincere."
James 3:17

Wisdom. You will read that word often in this book. Perhaps your greatest need throughout your baby's first year is wisdom—even if you've been through this before with another baby. Even if you think that all you really need is sleep or, for heaven's sake, a shower. What you truly need every moment of every day is wisdom.

I can't think of a better time to get down on your knees and beg the good Lord for wisdom than when you are facing your child's first immunizations. As Dr. Johnston shared, there is much controversy in the media, on bookshelves, and likely in your neighborhood playgroup about what is best for children in regard to vaccinations. To be honest, I thought long and hard about how we could write a book about baby's first year without addressing this hot topic at all. I didn't want to face the passionate hearts on either side of this discussion. But we couldn't write a helpful and comprehensive book for new moms without covering this important topic, so here we are.

Dr. Johnston did a wonderful job sharing the medical facts surrounding each of your child's scheduled vaccines. Since she is a physician, I'm sure you can understand her passion on the subject. Her point of view, having seen hundreds of patients, is a bit different than ours as moms trying to avoid any and every harm that might befall our little ones. But remember, Dr. Johnston is also that mom who wants to protect her child. In that way, she possesses a unique and thorough perspective on the subject. Perspective. That's what I hope we can help you gain as you consider immunizations.

As we've said before, the Internet is a wonderful and dangerous tool. You will definitely find articles that claim to prove that vaccinations are dangerous for children. You will find forums where moms insist their child became ill after receiving shots. You will also find research and medical studies that report no concrete evidence for those claims. You can easily be left in a state of confusion.

Our heart for this resource is to provide the facts and encourage you to seek the Lord for his will for your baby and your family. If you feel a resistance in your heart to having your child follow the recommended vaccination schedule, first ask yourself why you are resistant. Is it true fear? Is it simply because all your friends say you shouldn't do it? Do you truly believe these shots will harm your child?

Although this issue may seem to be the biggest mountain of decision you will have to climb, honestly it's only the first of many—for the next eighteen years and more. I encourage you to walk through the following process of decision-making on this and any other major issues you face.

❑ Check yourself: What are you really feeling about the issue?

❑ Check the facts: Carefully research the issue, looking only to credited sources.

❑ Check with your spouse (or support system): Ask close loved ones (not all your girlfriends) their feelings on the issue.

❑ Check with your doctor: Hopefully you've built trust with your baby's pediatrician and will trust her recommendations or feel comfortable asking for an alternate plan if necessary.

❑ Check your spirit: Bathe the issue in prayer, asking God who gives wisdom liberally to all who ask for it.

As you process, think back to this month's Scripture from James. The wisdom that comes from heaven is peace-loving. It's not confusing. Holy Spirit wisdom is submissive. It's not argumentative or controversial. Your word from the Lord will be impartial. It's not based on what others think.

I personally followed the immunization schedule recommended by my doctor and the AAP. I simply didn't have a strong feeling in my heart that these shots would be harming my children. I believed wholeheartedly that they would be protecting my children from illness. If you do have fear or questions regarding vaccinations, it is completely understandable. We cannot, however, let fear drive our decision making as parents. Fear leads to confusion and reaction instead of careful consideration and pro-action. Ask the Lord for peace as you consider what is before you. Trust that he will lead you, and even more, trust that he will protect your child.

With every shot that was given to my two children, I prayed the following prayer. Although I didn't have a strong feeling about immunizations and peacefully agreed to the recommended schedule, I take very seriously anything that is put into my children's bodies. Laying this request before the Lord gave me peace and sure confidence as they received each vaccine.

> *Dear Lord,*
> *Thank you for the wisdom and medical advancements that you have provided for our safety. I ask you to cover my baby right now. May these vaccines do everything they are supposed to do to protect my child—nothing more, nothing less. I am thankful for medical means, but I know that ultimately you are our Protector. Once again, I place my baby in the care of you, our Great Physician. Amen.*

Settling In

Whether you choose to fall into a routine naturally or you follow a more strict scheduling method, by now you should be experiencing more predictable days. This breakthrough will do wonders for you and your baby. You will likely begin to enjoy your days more now that you know what to expect. If your baby is having a tough time with eating or sleeping, and you find that you are not yet settling in, don't get discouraged. Although this milestone is common, there are exceptions. Some babies have a much harder time adjusting, and it takes longer. Trust that you will get there, and ask the Lord for an extra measure of grace in the meantime.

Perhaps one of the hardest adjustments of new motherhood is finding time for yourself. You feel as though the whole world (although only one or maybe a few lives) is depending on you every moment of every day. There's no time to eat or shower, much less have quiet time or exercise. If only motherhood came with the power to stop time—I promise I wouldn't abuse it—I would be able to eat at designated mealtimes and wash my hair daily. But alas, we are left with an ever-advancing clock, ticking away each minute of the day rapidly. I encourage you to pray and ask God to give you a strategy for making time for him and for yourself. He will show you ways to refuel and rejuvenate with minimal effort, and I believe he will exponentially increase any efforts you make. Don't get caught up in thinking you need to spend an hour a day reading the Bible and praying. There is no set requirement from God for the time we spend with him. He craves our company and will bless any time we sacrifice to choose him.

As if it wasn't hard enough to find quiet time every day, add in the desire to exercise, and you're a stressed-out mess. We also need to ask God for strategies for this important area of our total well-being as moms. God desires for us to be whole—body, mind, and spirit. You may think that's a nearly impossible goal. But with God, all things are possible (Matt. 19:26). It is his divine will for us to live well-balanced lives. Therefore, he will provide ways for us to achieve this goal as we seek him.

Simple Strategies for Mommy Time

· Read the Bible out loud to your baby. This way you both get the Word.
· Find a short devotional to read daily. (Suggestions are listed in the Appendix.)
· Pray continually as you move through your day. In the car . . . doing laundry . . .
· Go for walks with your little one. Baby will love the fresh air.
· Find a simple video workout on DVD or Netflix. Put baby in a swing while you exercise.
· Ask your husband or family member to watch baby while you go to the gym a few times a week.
· Shower in the evening while baby is asleep. Going to bed clean is refreshing to mind and body.

If your baby is having a tough time adjusting, please be kind to yourself. It's likely not anything you have or haven't done. Ask God to confirm in your heart that you are doing your best for your baby. Then let go of any feelings of inadequacy or guilt. For some babies, it's just hard. Whether it's digestive issues or difficulty with sleep, it's perfectly normal for a baby not to have fallen into a routine by this point. Talk to your doctor about any concerns, and seek support from your family and friends as you continue to walk through this season. It will not last forever. I can promise you that.

Sibling Tips

Already have a little one in your home? You might be experiencing sibling jealousy at this point. A few months ago, as I went to put the baby down for a nap, my four-year-old started to have a meltdown. It was obvious to me that she needed my attention, yet I needed to get the baby to sleep. My nine-month-old took a little coaxing to get to sleep at that stage, so I was overwhelmed trying to figure out how to meet both of their immediate needs. I left my screaming preschooler and took the baby up to his room. As I stood, swaying with my little one, I desperately asked the Lord what to do. I typically would not put him down wide awake, as he would scream so long that a nap would be impossible. But I didn't have time to rock him to a drowsy state as I normally would. My little girl needed me—quick. So I prayed, and I heard the Lord say, "Put him down. I'll take care of him." So I laid him wide awake in his bed and left the room. He cried as I exited, but by the time I was downstairs holding my daughter in my lap, there was silence from his room. He was asleep, and she was content with mommy's undivided attention.

As you focus much of your attention on your new baby, your other child (or children) may feel neglected. Keep in mind that there may be times, like the one I just shared, that your other children need a little extra attention. But even if you purpose to give your toddler or preschooler adequate attention, it may never be enough now that they are competing with another person. Try to involve your older child in as much of your activity with baby as you can. Give her special jobs to do or ask her to choose what toy to play with next. If you can, plan special one-on-one time with each of your children so they receive the benefit of your undivided attention during this transitional time. Eventually, everyone will fall into a rhythm as a family. Most importantly, speak words of love and affirmation to your child so she understands that although circumstances have changed, your love for her has not.

Shopping for Baby at Two Months

You may have already figured out that buying a lot of clothing for baby in the early stages is a mistake. Your child is growing at a rapid pace, and he will not be able to wear many items for that long. Focus on simple, staple items such as bodysuits and pajamas with a few "going out" outfits for special outings or occasions. Below is a list of newborn essentials. I realize that most moms (myself included) will stock their baby's closet way beyond these minimalist recommendations. My goal here is to give you an idea of how little you can get by with. Any additions you make to your baby's wardrobe are your prerogative (and pleasure, I'm sure).

Newborn Essentials

Fall/Winter	Spring/Summer
Bodysuits (long-sleeved)	Bodysuits (short-sleeved)
Pajamas	Pajamas (bodysuits work just fine for
Soft pants	pjs in the summer)
Socks	Hat
Jacket	2 to 3 special outfits
Hat	
2 to 3 special outfits	

If you haven't already, be sure to look for consignment sales in your area where you can purchase gently used children's clothing for a fraction of the retail cost. This is also a great place to find deals on baby gear. Once you've moved through your own child's clothing and gear, you can join your local sale and make a bit of cash yourself. Each season, I sell my children's clothes and use the money I make to purchase the next season's clothes. Not only am I helping to recycle clothing for others, but I am recycling my budget as well.

Are you saddened by the fact that your baby is going to grow out of clothes faster than you can buy them? Savor these days. They will fly by. Before you know it, your little one will cut teeth and start crawling. You cannot get these early days back. Don't let them pass you by without soaking up the joy of each moment.

Prayer Concerns

Direction regarding immunizations

Baby's routine

Finding mommy time

A Prayer for This Month

Dear Lord,

Thank you that I can see a light at the end of this tunnel. Your steadfast grace has gotten me through every day and night thus far. I trust that you will continue to pour it over me. Father, give me peace and direction regarding immunizations. I want to hear clearly what you are saying for our baby. Help me eliminate the noise that surrounds me so I can hear from you on this and every issue I will face. Give me strategies for finding time to take care of myself—body, mind, and soul. I know a well-balanced life will help me be a better mom. I am so thankful to have you walking with me on this journey. Amen.

Write your own prayer of reflection.

Journal

The Hope of Sleep

Baby Stats

By three months, babies range from 9 to 15 pounds (4.5–7 kg) in weight and approximately 21½ to 24½ inches (55–62 cm) in length. Once again, these numbers are averages, so do not be too concerned if your baby's stats fall outside of this range. Talk with your doctor about any questions you have regarding his growth.

This is still a time of rapid growth and development. You can expect your child to have gained about two pounds per month for the first three months or so.

Development Checker at Three Months

Typical Skills

❑ Recognizes your face

❑ Holds head steady and turns to sound

❑ Visually tracks objects

❑ Raises head and chest when lying on stomach

Concerning Signs

❑ No smiling to the sound of a parent's voice

❑ Unable to support head

❑ Frequently crosses eyes

There are many developmental milestones on the horizon as your baby begins to soak in the world around him. This stage can be a lot of fun as you begin to reap the benefits of your interaction with baby.

Vision

Your baby may have brief crossing of the eyes as he tries to focus; however, if crossing lasts longer or occurs frequently, it could indicate a concern. Additionally, if you notice one of your baby's eyes is lazy or droopy, you should inform your pediatrician. Talk with your doctor if you notice either of these conditions to see if she would recommend an ophthalmologic consult. Because a baby's vision takes time to develop, these specialists would not typically see a baby before three months, making this the ideal time to look into any possible vision problems.

Language

All the hard work you've been doing for the past two months is beginning to pay off! You will start to notice baby smiling and even cooing aloud for you when he is spoken to. Talk to your baby in soothing tones when he is upset, and you will find that he will listen. Babies are very observant and learn from an early age the speech patterns of their parents.

Movement

Head strength. One of the most important motor skill developments in this early stage is good head control. Your baby should be allowed to have playtime on his tummy every day. By two months, he may only be able to lift and turn his head for just a few seconds. But this practice will help him strengthen his neck and trunk muscles. Until his strength is good, you should take care to support his head and body at all times. Even after your baby gets better at holding his head up, he can still suddenly jerk or flail back. By three months, your baby should be able to pick up his head and look around while lying on his chest. However, it takes a little longer to develop the strength and control to lift up his head while lying on his back. If you try to pull a newborn from lying down to sitting up at one month of age, his head will fall back. By four months, most babies can hold their heads steady when being pulled gently from a lying to sitting position. This development of neck strength is welcome news for both you and baby. For parents, it will give some freedom from having to hold your baby so carefully when moving around. For babies, it is an increasing opportunity to explore their surroundings.

Tummy time. Moms are encouraged to make sure babies have daily tummy time. Although it becomes increasingly important as baby gets older, tummy time can start as soon as you bring him home from the hospital. Tummy time is when baby is placed on his tummy to play while someone is watching him. Babies should not be left alone on their tummies. And again, babies should not sleep on their bellies at this age, due to the risk of SIDS. Always remember: place baby on his back to sleep and on his tummy to play.

Tummy time is important for proper development of motor skills. By three months, a baby should easily be able to lift his head off the floor when lying on his stomach. We encourage that babies have tummy time two to three times per day for about five minutes each time at first. Eventually, as your baby begins to play, his tummy time can increase. At that point, it is encouraged to allow your baby to have tummy time for at least ten to twenty minutes per day.

Tummy time may also help prevent the development of positional plagiocephaly, or flattening of the back of the head. If you do notice that your baby's head has misshapen areas, you should see your doctor right away. Rarely, this can be a sign of premature fusion of the bones of the skull, and your doctor may want to run tests to rule it out. Usually, though, this is a simple cosmetic issue and will correct over time with just a little effort.

To prevent flattening of the head, try alternating which end of the bed you place your baby's head. Because he may be attracted to a light or an interesting object in his room, alternating the position will encourage varying positions of his gaze. Additionally, alternating which way your baby is held while feeding may help prevent recurrent pressure on the same area of his head. Avoid allowing babies to lay flat too long in a swing, car seat, or bouncy seat, as this position may add extra pressure to the back of the head and cause flattening.

Baby Care

Feeding

If you're one of the lucky few, your baby is on track with a consistent schedule by now. With your milk well established and your baby becoming a more efficient eater, breastfeeding should take between fifteen and thirty minutes at each feeding. If your baby is small for her age and either nursing too rapidly (done eating after five to ten minutes) or taking too long to feed (thirty minutes or more), talk with your doctor about possible underlying issues. Many formula-fed babies may only wake once for an overnight feeding at this point. Breastfeeding babies may still have two to three overnight feedings at the three-month mark. Breastfeeding babies may also still want to cluster feed at times, eating every thirty minutes to an hour. Refer to the sample schedules later in this chapter for more information about how much and how often baby may be eating at this point.

If your baby is exclusively breastfed, he should be started on a daily vitamin D supplement no later than two months of age. As explained in Month One, this will help prevent vitamin deficiency leading to rickets. It may be tempting at this point to give your baby rice cereal to help him sleep through the night; however, this practice is discouraged. All solid foods should be saved until at least four to six months of age.

Hopefully, if you are breastfeeding, it's become second nature to you by now. If you are still experiencing difficulty, it's never too late to talk with your pediatrician or seek the counsel of a lactation consultant. Breastfeeding is something worth fighting for. Gather your army and continue to do what you can to thrive in feeding your child. However, if you've given it everything you've got, there is no shame in moving ahead with formula. At some point, you will need to determine what is best for you and your baby. For example, if your supply is dropping at this point, and your baby is only getting two to three ounces of breast milk a day, it may not be enough of a benefit to make it worth the struggle. It's okay to move to formula-feeding if this is the case. You shouldn't feel bad about having to put your baby on formula if your body is telling you that it can't make enough milk. Seek as much help and counsel as possible, but in the end, ask God for wisdom to know if and when it's time to transition to formula. Refer to the Baby's First Year at a Glance chart at the beginning of this book for information on how much your baby should be eating at this stage.

Sleep and Schedules

Babies will usually continue to sleep more than play at this age. Your baby may still be taking three to four naps a day. Signs that he may need a nap include avoiding eye contact with you, crying or fussing, grunting, squirming, and rubbing his eyes.

While some babies may not have regular sleep schedules until six months of age, there are some who are ready for "sleep training" by two or three months. As mentioned in Month Two, there are many resources for new families on setting a schedule. Some suggest a very regimented schedule, while others suggest no schedule at all. I encourage moms to ask friends and family what worked for them and to read for themselves. I find that most families end up with their own unique plan. Most babies by two or three months of age begin to show their own patterns of eating and sleeping, so getting your baby on a schedule may happen naturally. Many babies will sleep for longer periods at night, up to six to eight hours in a row by three months of age.

There is no medical benefit to having babies on a schedule at this age. Sure, it is nice for the parents. But babies on a strict schedule are not more "healthy" in some way than babies with an erratic sleep schedule. Sleep training a baby to the right environment is more important than training him to a certain time schedule. Regardless of the timing of naps and feedings, the location and routine to get to sleep can be established. After your baby has fed and played, rock him to a drowsy-but-awake state, then put baby in his own bed and allow him to fall asleep on his own. This kind of early sleep training will allow you to "pay it forward" so to speak, as babies who don't learn this skill now tend to still not have this skill at eight to nine months of age.

Diapering

You've likely gotten a handle on changing your baby's diaper. One word of caution: the weight range indicated on the diaper box is just that—a range. And often times, although your baby falls within the range for a specific diaper size, his volume of urine or stool far outweighs said diaper's absorption ability. In other words, pay close attention to baby's wet and dirty diapers. If they seem to be cutting it close, it's time to up his diaper size. When in doubt, try a bigger diaper. You'll avoid a lot of blowouts this way.

Bathing

Your baby may actually begin to enjoy baths at this stage. Continue bathing him as often as you are comfortable. Every other day or a few times a week is sufficient unless you have a strong desire to bathe him daily. Especially if you bathe him daily, keep an eye on baby's skin condition, as frequent baths can lead to dryness. Make sure to moisturize him after each bath. He may have very sensitive skin, so watch out for products containing any fragrances or dyes.

Eczema. If you notice severe dry patches or raised bumps on baby's skin, this could indicate eczema. Eczema is simply a severe form of dry skin that is treated easily by avoiding harsh bath products, bathing less frequently, and moisturizing daily. One possible treatment is over-the-counter 1 percent hydrocortisone cream for the driest areas. Just apply a thin layer to the patch of eczema twice daily. These topical steroids should not be used for more than two weeks in a row without contacting your baby's doctor. Talk to your doctor if you think your baby could have eczema to find out what she would recommend as treatment.

Cleaning baby's ears. It is a good idea to clean baby's ears after each bath. Be extremely careful when using Q-tips, and use safety swabs when possible. These special tools have a larger tip, which helps to avoid going deep into baby's ear. Never place the cotton swab down into the baby's ear canals. It is not uncommon for a baby's eardrum to be punctured when a caregiver goes a little too far into the canal with the Q-tip. You should only clean what earwax you can see from the outside. Try lightly wetting the end of the swab before cleaning each ear.

Baby Safety

Bathtub. If you hang a sign near baby's bathtub, it should read "slippery when wet" as a reminder that you can very easily lose your grip on your little one as he begins to splash, kick, and wiggle more in the bath. Take extra care in handling your baby, keeping in mind that he'll be slippery and more mobile now. Never leave your baby unattended in the bath. Don't forget to check the temperature of the water so that it doesn't get too hot or too cold for baby. Remember his tolerance of temperature varies from yours.

High surfaces. Although your baby will probably not start rolling over until next month, he may be practicing. Never leave your baby unattended on a bed, couch, or changing table. You'll be surprised how quickly he will find a way to move to explore his surroundings. This is the age we often hear stories about babies rolling off of something because parents think they are not yet able.

Expectations for Your Doctor Visits

Although you probably felt like you were going to visit the doctor weekly for the rest of your child's life, you actually do not have a well visit this month. Your baby will see the doctor again at four months and then six months.

If you have any concerns, do not hesitate to put in a call to your pediatrician. There are no stupid questions for new moms. Everything that is going on inside your little one is such a mystery. No one will judge you or laugh at you for asking a seemingly silly question. Use your motherly instincts and ask when you need to ask. Honestly, we'd rather you call than Google your question and get inaccurate information.

Reasons to Call Your Pediatrician

At this point, you will not have a doctor visit every month. Here are a few reasons to call your pediatrician in between visits:

- Excessive crying or fussiness (more than typical, or inconsolable).
- Decreased feeding.
- Constipation that is not resolved with regular home remedies such as juice or corn syrup.
- Any fevers that aren't related to a simple cold or that persist more than two to three days.

Common Questions You May Have This Month

My baby's belly button seems to be bulging out. Is this just the way it is, or could there be something wrong?

It could be an umbilical hernia. Some babies by two months may have a hernia at their belly button. This can be detected shortly after birth, but by two months it can look quite dramatic. Umbilical hernias are caused when a hole or weak area in the muscle wall surrounding the belly button allows tissue to bulge out. This is most noticed when a baby is crying or straining, and there is increased pressure in the abdomen. As long as you can easily "reduce" or push the belly button down again, there is no need for concern. Treatment is not recommended, as most umbilical hernias will self-correct by preschool age. If your child still has his umbilical hernia by kindergarten, surgical closure may be needed. Contrary to popular belief, taping the area or affixing a coin to the belly with tape is not helpful and not recommended.

Are my baby's eyes going to change color?

Most new parents are very interested in what color their baby's eyes are going to be. The colored part of the eye, or iris, is determined by a number of factors. Genetically, if both parents have blue eyes, then their child can be expected to have blue eyes, though this is not always true. The children of two parents with brown eyes will nearly always have brown eyes. If mom and dad have different eye colors, there is a pretty even split between what color the child's eyes will be. In general, a baby's eyes will look deep blue or grey at first, regardless of his skin color. Over the next six months, the amount of melanin (color pigment) in the iris will change. Your baby's eyes may turn to a lighter blue or change to green or brown. In most babies, their final eye color is determined by about one year of age.

I've read in several baby books that it is best to allow babies to play after they eat and then put them down for a nap rather than feeding them directly before a nap. Is this the best way to schedule a baby?

It's not so much that it's "best," but that it's just what most babies want to do anyway at this age. Most babies are ready to eat as soon as they wake up from a nap, so it makes sense that they wouldn't be tired again immediately after that feeding.

Most babies by three months will stay awake for at least one to two hours before needing to go down for the next nap.

Mommy Care

Up to 70 percent of women will experience postpartum blues. While it's normal to feel like a hormonal, sleep-deprived mess for the first week or two, as you begin to get a little more sleep and a little more settled, you should start to feel more like yourself. The exact cause of postpartum blues is unknown, but it is thought to be a combination of hormonal changes and sleep deprivation.

Common symptoms of postpartum blues:

• Irritability

• Crying spells

• Insomnia

• Mood changes

• Anxiety

If you continue to feel teary and overwhelmed for more than two weeks, or you feel empty or nothing when you look at your child, this is not normal and could be a sign of postpartum depression. If you have any thoughts of wanting to hurt yourself or your baby, it is a sign of significant postpartum depression. It is important to understand that these feelings are not the result of your hormones when they last beyond the first couple of weeks.

Many women will say that they would never hurt their baby or themselves, but they feel the need to run away or escape. They feel their family would be better off without them. These types of thought patterns are highly suggestive of postpartum depression as well.

As Christians, it can be hard to admit we are experiencing depression because we mistakenly view it as only a spiritual issue. The truth is, postpartum depression is a serious medical condition and requires treatment. It is essential to treat postpartum depression thoroughly and immediately, so you can fully bond with your baby. I find so many women who want to blame their depression on something: their hormones, their husband, or their circumstances. While these factors may have helped trigger depression, it should be treated as a separate medical condition. It is important to seek medical attention if you believe you are experiencing depression so you can understand your unique needs.

Risk factors for postpartum depression include:

- History of depression
- Social stressors
- Diabetes
- Not breastfeeding
- Marital conflict
- Lack of social support
- Unplanned pregnancy

Initial treatment can include social support, rest (sleep), and exercise. Additional treatment can include therapy or mild antidepressant medications. Some moms are very resistant to the idea of medication, but try to put it in perspective. If you had high blood pressure, and diet and exercise didn't improve your condition, would you take medicine? Hopefully, the answer is yes. Yes, you should pray for healing of the depression and meditate on Scriptures to renew your mind, but you should also realize that you may need medication to treat this medical condition. Just like other medical conditions, healing often comes through a combination and partnership of both medical and spiritual means.

If you do start to take medication, it is usually best to take it for at least a year, or the risk of relapse increases. Since postpartum depression seems to be triggered by the hormonal shifts at delivery, multiple studies that tried to treat the depression with replacement hormones have been completed. However, no specific hormone combination has been found to be effective for treatment.

Symptoms of postpartum depression include:

- Loss of appetite
- Loss of energy
- Loss of libido
- Feelings of guilt
- Feelings of emptiness or sadness

- Apathy towards hobbies
- Feeling isolated
- Avoiding family and friends
- Thoughts of harming self or baby (even if no intent of acting on them)
- Feelings of failure to be a good mother

Keep in mind that depression manifests in different ways for different people. If you are experiencing any of these symptoms or others not listed here that could be described as atypical for you, please talk with your doctor. You will find a postpartum depression scale that is often used in screening for PPD in the Appendix of this book. Complete the scale and discuss your results with your OB. This should be one of the most amazing and rewarding times in your life. Seek treatment before depression robs you of enjoying these precious months with your sweet baby.

The following story is a wonderful example of how one mom sought both medical and spiritual help through her battle with postpartum depression. Please keep in mind as you read that your journey may look very different. If you are experiencing PPD but do not receive this immediate healing through prayer, do not be discouraged. God has different plans for each of our lives. He will meet you where you are within your battle with PPD, but your process may look different than it does for others. Trust him along your journey.

A Real-Life Story

Postpartum Depression

Crista, mom to Claire and Graham

After my first baby arrived, I was swallowed up by postpartum depression. Nothing in my life felt normal. I had a very fussy infant with breastfeeding problems,

I wasn't sleeping (duh) or eating well, and I ended up hiding in my house because I didn't want to see or talk to anyone. This was a complete one-eighty from the person I had been several months prior. Things were not right, but I didn't know how to move out of that dark place. I felt trapped.

I asked my OB for help with medication, and she was happy to discuss my options. She prescribed Lexapro to help level me out. I took the samples she gave me but never filled the prescription. I didn't feel any change after those first two weeks, so I figured the medication wasn't working. I didn't know it took thirty days for the drugs to get to work in my system and start making a difference.

Six months later, I was at my wits' end. Things had only gotten worse and I was just barely surviving. I called my OB again and asked her to rewrite my prescription. This time I filled it and stayed with it. Once the medication was working in my body, I could tell a huge difference. I felt much more normal. The absence of crazy mood swings and outbursts of tears was a major improvement.

I went on with life and thought everything was fine. But months later, I started to feel that familiar, ugly darkness creep in on me again. I was confused because I thought that my problem was a chemical imbalance. Come to find out, depression is not just a single-layer issue; it affects body, soul, *and* spirit. I had only been treating the body, but my soul and spirit were also in need of healing. My husband had been very hurt over those months of my dealing with depression, and he was so eager for me to be healthy again. He asked if I would consider having someone at our church pray for me. I shot him a cutting glance and made him feel stupid for suggesting such a thing. (This wasn't like me—I have loved and followed hard after Jesus for many years, and I believe in the power of prayer.) Finally, after a few weeks of asking me to consider prayer, I gave in to my husband. Honestly, I just wanted to shut him up.

We agreed that at the very next church service I would go forward for prayer and tell someone about my problem. Things didn't quite turn out like we had planned. . . . The next service involved praying in groups for each others' needs, *not* going to the front for one-on-one prayer. I was so mad, but I just went for it. I told a group of people I didn't know about the darkest issue of my life and asked them to pray. I wasn't expecting anything. But I sure got something.

As these unknown people prayed for me, I felt a heaviness lift off my back and shoulders. I felt my lungs inflate fully, and when I opened my eyes, the room seemed much brighter than before. It was like something had its iron claw dug into my heart all those months, and all of a sudden it was gone. The liquid love of God poured over me and filled in the holes in my heart where darkness had tried to kill me. I was delivered from this *thing* that I didn't even know was attached to me.

Depression is ugly. It lies to you and steals from you. It wants to kill you. Don't let it. Medical treatment and sometimes medication is a great place to start. I thank God for helpful medication and doctors who know what they are doing. But, along with physical treatment, you need to attend to your heart, mind, and spirit. Fill your day with uplifting music, with encouraging words, and with people who will support you. Call out to God, and let other people pray for you. If you take baby steps in all three layers of your being, you'll be on the right track.

Truth for the Journey

"My flesh and my heart may fail, but God is the strength of my heart and my portion forever." Psalm 73:26

Becoming a new mom does something extraordinary to your heart. Never before have you felt such a deep connection to another human being. Sure, you are connected to your spouse, but this is different. This is your own flesh and blood. Your offspring. It is part of God's beautiful design that a mother who carries a baby within her womb for nine months should feel so physically and emotionally connected to that life even after they are "separated." With your heart now open wider than it's ever been before, it is also vulnerable to feelings of lack and inadequacy. You desire so deeply to be everything your little one needs, yet you can't possibly, in your own strength, measure up. Are you overcome by the reality of your weakness? Has motherhood illuminated your shortcomings? Our flesh and our heart may fail, but there is great news for us mamas. God is the strength of our heart and our portion (our provision for every need) forever!

With that in mind, you can be reminded that he supplies everything you need, daily, to be a great mom for your baby. This includes strength, energy, wisdom, and strategy (for starters). You will never lack what you need in motherhood if you rely on God's provision. This does not mean you will be the perfect mother. It simply means, by his grace, you will be everything your child needs—shortcomings and all. Because God works all things together for our good—that includes using our mothering weaknesses for good in our lives and in the lives of our children.

If you haven't already, find a group of moms in your area to connect with. I share in depth about finding your "mom tribe" later in Month Eleven. Flip ahead to read that encouragement now. You may feel overwhelmed at the thought of nurturing relationships beyond that of your new little one, but having a community of moms around you is crucial to thriving through this year and the years to come. Read the ideas and advice given and simply keep your eyes and ears open for women in your sphere. This is yet another need that God will fill as you rely on him.

Scheduling Strategy

Before I share my thoughts on a scheduling strategy, let me first say that I had very different points of view with each of my babies. With my daughter (my firstborn), I aimed to follow a popular book on sleep and scheduling that is pretty regimented. As I shared in the Introduction, when my efforts fell short of "success," I felt like a failure. The Lord quickly led me to lay aside my goal to achieve scheduling perfection and simply take principles I had read or heard about from friends and seek him for a strategy that was unique to my baby and our family. Within a few weeks, we fell into a natural routine, and by six to eight months of age, my once-horrible napper had become a champion sleeper. By the time my son entered the family, I had strayed far, far away from the school of thought that hyper-scheduling is best. Add to this newfound freedom of thought the reality of life with two (one in preschool), and we swung our pendulum completely to the other side. As we near the one-year mark, I can honestly say that I don't believe there is a right or wrong way to approach scheduling. As Dr. Johnston mentioned, most babies will fall into a natural routine around three or so months with a little guidance. At the end of the day, what really matters is that you are able to move through your days with peace and confidence. Whatever that looks like for you and your family is the best approach.

The reality is, life outside your womb is still very new to your baby. You've been gently guiding him from day one on eating, sleeping, playing, and development. As you both begin to settle in, you can increase your strategy to further help your baby adjust to his surroundings. If you begin to look at scheduling as "gentle guidance" rather than an über-regimented military task, you will more easily find a rhythm that is driven by wisdom and peace rather than by rules and condemnation.

Practically speaking, consistency is key. One of the very first things my husband and I did with both of our babies was to establish a bedtime routine. Somewhere between two and three months is a great time to implement this strategy. In order to help your baby understand the difference between day and night, or naptime and bedtime, work toward a consistent routine when putting baby down at night.

Steps to Establish a Bedtime Routine

1. *Decide on a bedtime and stick to it.* Even if your baby's feeding schedule has been off for the day, adjust his afternoon toward a specific bedtime.

2. *Give baby a bath.* If you choose to bathe your baby daily, plan a warm bath as part of your routine. If you are not bathing your child every day, include a bath when desired.

3. *Put on soothing lullaby music.* You may find it helps to play the same music nightly as part of the routine. Your baby will eventually associate this music with bedtime. You may not want to keep the music on as baby is falling asleep, as it could become a sleep prop. A fan or other "white noise" works well, as it is less of a prop and more about creating an environment.

4. *Change baby's diaper and put on snuggly jammies.* Changing your baby's clothes is a big part of establishing this routine.

5. *Create a quiet mood.* Keep lights low and use a soft voice when talking to baby as you move through your routine.

6. *Feed baby and rock him for a bit.* This one-on-one time with you is not only key, it's precious to you and to him.

7. *Lay him down in his bed.* It is your choice whether you lay baby down awake or wait until he falls asleep. This part of the routine may evolve as baby grows. You can begin by rocking baby to sleep and gradually put him down more and more alert until he is eventually able to go into his bed awake and fall asleep on his own. It is best to do this between three and six months. If you wait much longer, it will be much more difficult to get baby to fall asleep on his own.

In the morning, your baby may wake at different times for a while, which makes it hard to establish a start time to your day. At some point, baby will begin to wake up at a consistent hour, allowing you to begin your schedule at a certain time each day. For instance, if your baby is waking up some mornings at 5:30 A.M. and others at 6:30 A.M., and you feed baby immediately after he wakes up, your schedule will be different each day. I recommend adjusting your morning just as you do your evening to keep a consistent routine. Much of your plan will depend on how often your baby is eating and if he is breastfed or bottle-fed. Here are some examples of a possible routine.

Possible Breastfed Baby Schedule

5:30 A.M. – baby wakes up, eats for 15–25 minutes

7:00 A.M. – nap

8:30 A.M. – baby eats for 15–25 minutes

10:00 A.M. – nap

11:30 A.M. – baby eats for 15–25 minutes

1:00 P.M. – nap

2:30 P.M. – baby eats for 15–25 minutes

4:00 P.M. – nap

5:30 P.M. – baby eats for 15–25 minutes

8:30 P.M. – bedtime, baby eats for 15–25 minutes

(Your baby may still wake up once or twice in the night to eat.)

Possible Formula-Fed Baby Schedule

6:30 A.M. – baby wakes up, eats 6 ounces

8:00 A.M. – nap

10:00 A.M. – baby eats 5 ounces

12:00 P.M. – nap

2:00 P.M. – baby eats 5 ounces

4:00 P.M. – nap

5:30 P.M. – baby eats 5 ounces

8:30 P.M. – bedtime, eats 6 ounces

(Your baby may still wake up once or twice in the night to eat.)

Either of these sample schedules is doable at this stage. They vary by one hour depending on the time baby wakes up. It's important to remember that your baby cannot read the clock. He doesn't know exactly what time it is. So what's more important than exact times in guiding your baby through his day is routine and consistency. I also believe that if you want your baby to understand the difference between day and night, consistent bedtime and routine is important in guiding him toward sleeping through the night. Since every baby is different with differing needs, there is no guarantee on when he will sleep through the night, and you should not feel like a failure if it takes your baby longer than others. My daughter is four years old at the time of this writing. She slept through the night very early on and was quick to walk and talk. I know she is bright, but she is not at all interested in learning to recognize or write her letters. It would seem she is so far behind the other kids in her preschool class. But I know it just may take her longer to develop these skills. Similarly, your baby just might take more time to adjust to sleep and scheduling. Just because your baby is a "bad sleeper" at this age does not predict that he will have difficulty sleeping even three or four months from now. Just as it may take six months of trying to get an older child to eat peas, it also may take several months for a newborn to like his bed. We cannot feel badly when our children need time. Ask the Lord for daily wisdom, do what you feel is best to guide your child, and he will eventually get it. This is true of sleeping, learning letters, baseball, math, dance, writing . . . the list goes on and on.

Practical Tips for Formula-Feeding

If you are formula-feeding your baby, it's important to get a system in place for bottle preparation and cleanup. Premade formula is convenient but tends to be more expensive. If you plan ahead, powder formula can be easy to prep for baby.

The first thing you need to do is determine whether you want to serve the bottle warm or at room temperature. This choice may depend on your baby's preference. If you start out with formula at room temperature, he may do just fine on it for the long haul. For warm bottles, simply mix a large covered container of formula and keep it in the fridge. Pre-made powder formula can be stored in the fridge for up to 24 hours. When baby is ready to eat, fill his bottle with the desired amount of formula and heat up. We caution against using a microwave for warming a bottle, as it may leave hot pockets within the liquid that burn baby's mouth. Instead, fill a mug with hot tap water and submerge the bottle for a few minutes, or use a bottle warmer. For room-temperature bottles, fill enough bottles for the day with water so they will be ready for mixing on the spot. Talk to your doctor about whether or not you need to use filtered water in your area. In many areas, tap water is perfectly fine for baby's bottles. It is not recommended to use well water. Your water-filled bottles can be left on the kitchen counter or in a diaper bag. When it is time for baby to eat, simply add powder formula to the bottle and serve. We found that serving room-temperature formula was very convenient, and both of my babies did just fine with it. Considering the new bottles on the market with built-in formula storage, serving bottles at room temperature becomes very doable when you are on the go or when leaving baby with a sitter. Whether using pre-made or powder formula, pay close attention to the manufacturer's instructions on the packaging. Refer to the chart below for instructions on when to dispose of unused formula.

One of the biggest inconveniences of bottle-feeding is cleanup. It can be overwhelming to wash bottles all day long. If you can, keep enough bottles on hand to get you through the day. This way, you only have to wash them once a day. Keep a large bowl or tub in the sink, and deposit dirty bottles there throughout the day after rinsing. When you are ready to wash, fill the tub with hot, soapy water and clean with a bottle brush. Designate a clean area on your counter to leave bottles to dry on a clean towel or drying rack.

You'll find your own groove as you continue to bottle-feed your baby. Your preferences for formula prep, traveling with formula, and cleanup will come to light after a while. Do what works well for you, but most importantly, look for strategies that make life with formula a little easier.

Safe Formula Storage Guide*

Type	State	Storage
Powder	Unprepared	Covered well in cool, dry place
Powder	Prepared	Up to 24 hours in fridge
Powder	Leftover in bottle	Discard after 1 hour
Concentrated Liquid	Unprepared	Covered well in fridge
Concentrated Liquid	Prepared	Up to 48 hours in fridge
Concentrated Liquid	Leftover in bottle	Discard after 1 hour
Ready to Feed	Unprepared	At room temperature
Ready to Feed	Opened bottles	Up to 48 hours in fridge, covered
Ready to Feed	Leftover in bottle	Discard after 1 hour

*Information gathered from similac.com

Your baby is growing so fast, yet, despite your exhaustion, you probably still feel like the days are flying by. Make sure you are present, truly present throughout your days. Baby's itty bitty stage is gone in the blink of an eye, and you cannot get it back. If you feel too tired to really enjoy your little one, ask someone to come over and help so that you can get a good nap. Then you will be refreshed and recharged to enjoy quality time with your baby. Do not let yourself miss out on the bliss that comes with new motherhood because your body, soul, and spirit are in shock. There are people surrounding you—family members, church friends, or neighbors—who want to help you truly enjoy this time. Do not be too proud to ask them for the help they are ready to give.

Prayer Concerns

Falling into a routine

Ability to be present

Baby's development

A Prayer for This Month

Dear Lord,

I have often been trying to do this mommy thing in my own strength. Thank you for the reminder that you are my strength and my portion forever. I ask for your perfect strength to sustain me as I care for the precious gift you have given. Give me wisdom as we look to order our days. Help us to fall into a routine naturally. Sharpen my mind, Lord, to be present at all times for my child—even in the midst of sleep-deprived days. Thank you for developing this baby perfectly according to your will. Amen.

Write your own prayer of reflection.

_____

_____

_____

_____

_____

Journal

_____

_____

_____

_____

_____

_____

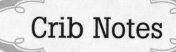

Crib Notes

Months One to Three

Mommy's Heart—Seek wisdom. Months one, two, and three are about enjoying your sweet baby while adjusting to your new normal. Rely on godly wisdom to help you find balance. It's available if you ask for it (James 1:5).

Baby's Development—Focus on breastfeeding technique, developing head and trunk strength through tummy time, encouraging baby's senses through visually stimulating pictures and the sound of your voice.

Feeding—Breastfeeding: 15–30 minutes every two to three hours. Bottle-feeding: 3–6 ounces every three to four hours.

Sleeping—10½–18 hours per day around the clock, with periods of one to three hours at a time spent awake.

Play—Sing and make faces to baby. He will love to watch you put on a show. Help baby develop his field of vision by moving a colorful toy in front of his face. He'll eventually follow it from side to side, up and down.

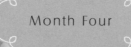

Constant Changes

Baby Stats

By four months, babies range from 12½ to 19 pounds (5.6–8.6 kg) in weight and approximately 23 to 26½ inches (60–68 cm) in length. Don't forget, these numbers are averages, so do not become too alarmed if your baby falls outside these ranges. Discuss any questions you have with your doctor.

Development Checker at Four Months

Typical Skills

❑ Smiles and laughs

❑ Coos in response to being spoken to

❑ Bears weight on legs when held up

❑ Starts to roll (usually from belly to back first)

❑ Holds head upright when lying on stomach

❑ Lifts chest off the floor when lying on stomach

❑ Holds a rattle

❑ Reaches out for toys

❑ Recognizes parents

❑ Begins to self-soothe

Concerning Signs

❑ Does not turn head toward sounds

❑ No social smiles

Language

Self-soothing. Always remember that crying is a means for your baby to communicate with you. He may cry when hungry, cold, or tired to let you know he needs something. And sometimes babies cry for no reason at all. Try to attend to the most common reasons for crying first. You may learn that different cries mean different needs for your baby. If you have taken care of all of his basic needs, and he is still fussy, you may have to leave him to self-soothe. Some babies, for example, always have a period of crying prior to falling asleep. It is perfectly fine to allow your baby to cry softly or fuss for a short period before he falls asleep. In fact, he may fall asleep more quickly if he is allowed to fuss than he would if he were being rocked, swayed, bounced, and talked to. The crying shouldn't last very long if he is tired. If his crying intensifies or lasts longer than fifteen to twenty minutes, check on your baby, as there may be something you missed. Most babies will have a specific fussy time of day. For example, many babies fuss more in the evenings. Listening to a crying baby for an extended period of time can be very frustrating. Allow your spouse or a family member to step in and help or relieve you if you become too overwhelmed. If your baby is inconsolable, he may be sick, and you should contact his pediatrician.

Movement

Rolling over. Daily tummy time is essential for helping your baby develop his motor milestones. By two to three months of age, he should be able to lift up his head from the floor. Next, he will start to push up and make "swimming" motions with his arms and legs. This will help strengthen his muscles and get him ready to roll over. Most babies roll first from their belly to their back, though it is normal if your baby rolls from back to belly first. Initially, he may just roll onto his side. Some babies get "stuck" and have to learn on their own how to tuck their arms and legs in to make it all the way over. This is an age where safety becomes very important. Be aware that babies learn to roll over quickly; even if he is unable to roll on one day, he might figure it out the very next. So never leave your baby unattended on a raised surface such as a bed, sofa, or changing table.

Grasp. At this stage, your baby is tightening his grip and learning to grasp objects. He should be able to grasp and shake a rattle by three months old. As this skill develops, he will reach for everything in sight, hoping to hold it in his tiny hands. Encourage your baby to explore his surroundings, but be extra careful to keep harmful objects or toys out of his reach.

Social Interaction

At this point, your baby is giving away his smiles at the grocery store. He gets excited to see other people, and because he is not yet experiencing stranger anxiety, his smiles are free for the taking. He is beginning to love interaction and will be thrilled when smiles are returned to him. If your baby does not regularly sport a social smile, discuss your concern with the doctor at his next checkup.

Baby Care
Feeding

Three- to four-month-olds should continue to receive breast milk or iron-fortified formula as their primary source of nutrition. In general, babies receive adequate nutrition from breast milk or formula and do not need solid foods until six months of age. Babies who are exclusively breastfed or who take less than 33 ounces of formula per day will continue to need a vitamin D supplement. Most four-month-olds will feed every three to four hours for fifteen to twenty minutes (breast) or take about 6 to 7 ounces (bottle) at each feeding during the day.

The current AAP recommendation is to wait to begin solid foods until six months of age. In the past, the recommendation has been to start solids as early as four months of age. In my opinion, there is a range of normal "readiness" for babies to begin solids, somewhere between four and six months old. We tried to wait until six months with my son, but by five months, he was sitting and practically begging for the food off of our plates. It was obvious he was ready. When introducing solids, the typical serving size for most babies is only one tablespoon. At first, he may only take one or two spoonfuls. Don't force him to finish every bite of his food—if he turns his head away or purses his lips together, he is done eating. Use only single-ingredient foods at first to determine if your child has an allergic reaction to each food. See Month Five for more information on starting baby on solid food.

If your baby was a preemie, he may still be taking a high-calorie formula to help with weight gain. Remind your doctor if your baby is still on this preemie formula, since between four and six months of age, babies can often transition to regular 20 kcal per ounce formula.

Sleep and Schedules

Some children can fall asleep anywhere at any time for the first two to three months. By four months, you may find that your baby is more alert and aware and doesn't sleep as well in unfamiliar places. Be consistent with his naptime and bedtime routines. Place him in bed when he is drowsy but not fully asleep so he can learn to fall asleep on his own. Allowing him to fall asleep in his own crib is recommended.

Your baby is moving towards a more predictable schedule now with three naps throughout the day, and may be sleeping through the night with only one feeding. Continue to focus on consistency and sleep environment if your baby is not yet moving towards these milestones. Every baby will achieve a predictable schedule at different points during this phase. Your gentle guidance will help him get there but do not allow yourself to feel like a bad mother if it takes him more time.

Teething

Although most babies do not get their first tooth until six months of age, your baby may start to show some initial signs of teething even now. This can include drooling more and gnawing on anything within his reach. Teething can persist for several months before you actually see a tooth. You can comfort baby with a teether or pacifier. If he seems to be in pain, you can give an age-appropriate dose of acetaminophen (Tylenol) or use a natural teething relief product such as Hyland's Teething Tablets. Topical, numbing medicines are fine to use, but they only provide immediate, short-term relief.

Illness

No matter how careful you are, your baby will get sick at some point. Often, a baby's first illness is a common cold. There are several factors that increase the risk of getting an upper respiratory infection. First, babies exposed to secondhand smoke tend to have more respiratory infections and ear infections. Even if you smoke outside, your baby still has an increased risk from the chemicals on your clothing, skin, and hair. Special care should be taken against smoking in an enclosed vehicle with a baby present.

By now, you may have returned to work and your baby is in day care. Babies that spend time in day care settings also tend to have more viral respiratory infections and ear infections due to exposure to other children and germs. Winter tends to be a harder time since more serious infections such as respiratory syncytial virus (RSV) are more prevalent in the colder months.

There are no over-the-counter cough and cold medications that are approved for babies. Most babies will feel better with simple home remedies such as elevating the head of their bed while sleeping, using nasal saline drops with bulb suction, and running a humidifier. Your baby may develop a mild fever (around 101 degrees or so) for the first few days while ill. He may take over-the-counter acetaminophen as needed per the instructions on the packaging. High fevers or fevers that persist for more than two to three days should be brought to the attention of your baby's doctor. She will likely want to see him in the office and make sure that the illness is not serious and does not require additional medication.

Many parents, especially those who have children in day care, become frustrated during the first year by how many times their child is ill. Some parents even wonder if their child has an immune deficiency or is allergic to something that could be making him sick. While this can be true, for most children it is just a normal part of growing up and is not because of any serious underlying medical condition. Children get an average of ten viral infections in the first two years of life, more if they are in day care or have school-age siblings. For children exposed frequently to germs, it can mean they are sick once a month. To a parent, it feels like their baby is "always" sick. In truth, it is usually a series of mild viral illnesses separated by a few days of wellness in between.

There's nothing more miserable to parents than to see their child sick and suffering. Fortunately, most babies will continue to play and smile despite a green, runny nose and a rattling cough. If your baby seems more sick than usual, alert his doctor right away.

Humidifiers. Particularly during an illness, you may want to use a cool-mist humidifier or vaporizer in your baby's room. This can help moisten the air and keep his nasal passages from becoming dry. Make sure you clean the humidifier according to the manufacturer's suggestions. Not cleaning a humidifier properly can lead to mold or mildew buildup in the machine, and running a machine that is blowing mold into the air may make your baby feel worse.

Baby Safety

Traveling with baby. You may be ready to venture out with baby to visit family and friends for the first time. If you'll be traveling on an airplane, be sure to bring a bag packed with anything you might need during the flight, such as a pacifier, extra clothes, and diapers. Dress your baby in clothing that comes on and off quickly and easily, since changing a baby in cramped quarters can be difficult. Breastfeeding or using a bottle or pacifier during takeoff and landing may help alleviate any pressure that your baby feels in his ears. Cabin noise, particularly during takeoff, can be quite loud. Your baby may benefit from a small amount of cotton placed in his ears. The AAP recommends that children under two years of age be restrained in a car seat on a plane just as they would be in a vehicle, however, this does require an extra ticket. Ask your airline when booking tickets about their policy for bringing car seats onto a plane, and make sure that your car seat is approved for use in airplanes.

Leaving baby in a car. No matter how often you are tempted to just run in and grab your dry cleaning or a pizza while leaving baby in the car, *never* leave an infant or child in a parked car, even for a few minutes. In the summer, cars can heat up to dangerous levels in a matter of minutes, even with the windows cracked open. Despite the inconvenience, always remove baby from the car when removing yourself.

Medication. You may use Tylenol (acetaminophen) for baby's fever or teething pain. Ibuprofen is not approved for use in babies before six months of age. You may continue to use gas drops as needed. There are no cough and cold medicines approved for infants at this age.

Expectations for Your Doctor Visits

Your baby should receive his four-month checkup soon. The vaccines that your baby will receive at his four-month visit are all boosters of vaccines that he received at his two-month visit. He will receive a liquid rotavirus vaccine and several injections. The shots will include boosters to DTaP, polio, Hib, hepatitis B, and pneumococcus. Some of these may be offered as a combination vaccine. You can expect similar reactions in your child, such as a small, sore place on his leg at the injection site and mild fussiness. Your baby's pediatrician will also review developmental milestones with you and give anticipatory guidance of what to expect in the coming months. Your next visit will be at six months of age.

Common Questions You May Have This Month

My baby is still not sleeping through the night. What can we do?

The four-month mark is a common time for parents to feel like their baby should be sleeping through the night. If your baby is still unable to sleep through the night, first make sure his environment is right. He is more than ready to sleep in his own bed. Make sure that the room is quiet and dim and that his before-bedtime routine is consistent. Don't fall into the trap of "keeping him awake during the day so he'll sleep at night." It almost always backfires. Babies who are well-rested during the day tend to be better sleepers at night. Stop feeding your baby in the middle of the night unless he is truly hungry. If he wakes up at 1:00 A.M. and 4:00 A.M., but he will only take ½ to 1 ounce of breast milk or formula each time, then he wasn't really hungry—he just needed soothing. Try giving him a pacifier, making gentle shushing sounds, and comforting him instead. Eventually, when he's no longer used to those midnight snacks, he will sleep through. If your baby is truly hungry and is demanding a full feeding, you should feed him.

My baby's been chewing on everything and drooling nonstop, but I still don't see any teeth. Why haven't his teeth come in yet?

Although the average age for baby's first tooth to appear is six months, it is possible for it to appear anywhere from four months old to after the first birthday. Babies at this age frequently "explore" with their mouths, so you may find that your baby constantly wants to bite and chew on his hands and toys. It doesn't necessarily mean that a tooth is pushing through. Be patient and keep watching—he may even get more than one tooth at a time. Expect that just before and during the early phases of tooth eruption, he may be fussier than usual and even bat at his ears or nose.

Mommy Care

Sex after Baby

When I see moms at their six-week postpartum visit, I discuss resuming sexual activity. As I broach this topic, I am greeted by a variety of responses, as different as the women themselves. Some laugh and say they have already resumed activities and all is good. More often, they give me a blank stare that says, "Are you kidding? I haven't slept in weeks. I am constantly coated in spit-up, and you want me to think about sex?" Whatever their initial attitude, I know that statistically, by three months postpartum, 90 percent of women have resumed sexual activity.

After you are fully healed and resume sexual activity, there is still a transitional time until things return to your new normal. Notice I said "new normal," because after children everything is different. Not necessarily worse or better, just different. If you keep waiting for your love life to be exactly how it was before the baby, you need to adjust your "sex-pectations."

Before you resume intercourse, it is important to be cleared by your doctor. If you resume activity before you are fully healed, it can prolong the healing process.

Whether you have pain with sex will depend on the type of your delivery. Most women experience some discomfort for three to six months. A vaginal delivery with no tears and a cesarean section without labor usually have the least pain. More severe vaginal lacerations often take the longest to fully recover, up to six months.

The most common types of pain are burning with insertion and sharp pain with deep thrust. The pain should get better with time and practice. Regularly using a water-based vaginal lubricant during the postpartum period is a must. If deep pain is an issue, try positions where the woman controls the depth of penetration.

While breastfeeding, the body's estrogen levels are low, leading to vaginal dryness and decreased lubrication for a lot of women. If you continue to have pain and dryness despite lubricant, see your physician. A small amount of estrogen vaginal cream can be prescribed to help restore your hormonal balance and improve lubrication.

Those who have had a C-section often have less pain in sex than those post vaginal delivery, but the first few sexual encounters may have more discomfort. Some of this pain is due to the previously discussed vaginal dryness from breastfeeding. Additionally, with a C-section, you've had incisions on your uterus, abdomen, and bladder and all these organs are attached to your vagina. Certain sexual positions may cause pulling on the internal healing scar tissue. When this happens attempt to reposition. It should slowly improve with time and the use of lubrication. If you are still having pain at six months postpartum, notify your provider. If you labored, pushed, and then had a C-section you often end up with the worst of both worlds: discomfort vaginally and abdominally during sex. In this situation, it is best to wait up to eight weeks before resuming intercourse instead of the usual recommendation of six weeks.

The most common sexual issue that women have postpartum is a lack of desire. The incidence of low libido at six months postpartum is 44 percent. However, only 10 percent reported being bothered by their lack of desire. For a lot of women, just knowing that it's normal not to feel overly amorous when they are six months postpartum is reassuring.

Usually, after the first couple of encounters, the pain will decrease and you should enjoy lovemaking again. If you enjoy sex when you have it and it doesn't hurt, that's a great start. It's okay that you don't necessarily spend all day thinking about it.

Attempt to set aside a scheduled day and time for intimacy. Notice I said "intimacy" and not just sex. For women, it is important to have time to connect with her partner to help her feel more amorous. And for any guys reading this: helping with the laundry and letting your wife take a nap is the *best* form of foreplay.

If at six months you are still having pain or not enjoying sexual intimacy, then it is time to see your doctor.

Common Reasons for Sexual Issues

Depression. If in addition to lack of sexual desire, you are also not enjoying any other hobbies, are feeling down, and are having crying spells, this could be a sign of postpartum depression. Talk about these feelings with your doctor.

Medications. Certain medications that treat high blood pressure, depression, and contraceptives can affect sex drive. If you are on medications, do not discontinue abruptly but instead talk to your doctor to determine if these could be affecting your libido. If so, request a change to an alternative treatment.

Fear of pregnancy. When you have been up all night with a colicky newborn, if you do start to feel a little amorous, the thought of getting pregnant again can sometimes be enough to nix any "vavoom" that you had percolating. Women often fear contraceptives might affect their breastfeeding, but there are multiple options that are both safe and effective.

While it's normal not to feel super-sexy in the postpartum phase, things will get better. Most women are back in the swing of things by about three months, but if you continue to experience pain and lack of sexual enjoyment at six months, follow up with your doctor for help.

Truth for the Journey

"And God is able to bless you abundantly, so that in all things at all times, having all that you need, you will abound in every good work." 2 Corinthians 9:8

You are getting to the really fun part of baby's first year. He's responding to you more and beginning to do journal-worthy things. You know . . . those things that warrant a note or entry into the baby book or baby's first year calendar you've been keeping close by. Laughs and coos, lifting his head, beginning to roll over— all of these developments will put joy in your heart in the midst of the continued stress of adjusting to life with a baby. Consider it a small reward for the countless hours of holding, feeding, clothing, and diapering you've already put in. The reward will only grow in the coming months as baby begins to wow you with seemingly daily developments.

Now that you are over the shock of adding a baby to your life, you should be getting past the place of merely surviving to a place of thriving as a mom. If you don't feel like you are there yet, don't be discouraged. His grace is abundant and will carry you every day.

Our key verse for this month is found in 2 Corinthians. In its original context, Paul was writing to the Corinthians about joy in giving. This particular verse follows the infamous passage about sowing and reaping: "Whoever sows sparingly will also reap sparingly, and whoever sows generously will also reap generously" (2 Cor. 9:6). We have always equated this verse with financial giving, and I do believe that was Paul's intent for this chapter of his letter to the Corinthian church. But I also know the God-breathed Word of Life goes far beyond its literal message. In this case, I believe the message is about much more than money. It's about anything, absolutely anything we choose to give of ourselves. Time, talent, treasure, and of course the daily, never-ending pouring out of ourselves for our children. As we sow generously into their lives, we will reap a harvest of grace and blessing. Verse 8 promises that he is able to "bless [us] abundantly, so that in all things at all times, having all that [we] need, [we] will abound in every good work." What a powerful promise! You will never, ever be lacking, mama, if you give of yourself generously and accept his promise of abundant grace.

Do you know what this means? It's time to step out of survival mode and begin to thrive in your days as a mom. If you feel you are not there yet (and if you have two or more at home, you may very well feel this way), it's okay. Continue to seek God for the grace and strategy that is available for you. The important thing is not to stay in survival mode for too long. You should be looking for the light at the end of the tunnel even if you do not see it up ahead quite yet.

Isaiah 40:11 says, "He tends to his flock like a shepherd: He gathers the lambs in his arms and carries them close to his heart; he gently leads those that have young." A mother shared this verse with me, saying it was the one that got her through days with her little ones. In *The Message,* this verse reads, "Like a shepherd, he will care for his flock, gathering the lambs in his arms, hugging them as he carries them, leading the nursing ewes to good pasture." Can you see it, friend? He is holding you close, hugging you as he carries you . . . leading you to good pasture. Not only are you not alone on this new journey of motherhood. You are being carried and led to a good place. Trust that he will not leave you in a state of sleep-deprived craziness. Look to him and he will guide you.

Consistent Flexibility

This is the season in which your little one will have constant changes. As soon as you get into a groove—especially if you are on a schedule—something happens and things need to shift. Eating habits, teething, illness—all of these things can affect your baby's routine. It is so important for moms to find the delicate balance between consistency and flexibility. This is where the leading of the Holy Spirit comes in. While you want to pursue order and routine with diligence for your baby, you must remain flexible enough to adjust in times of change. Ask for wisdom in each moment, and settle within your heart the fact that although you have a plan, you may need to adjust that plan based on baby's immediate needs.

We talked a bit last month about scheduling. Some moms desire a very predictable, rigid schedule, while others prefer no schedule at all. If you are seeking balance, you may find a flexible routine is a happy medium. Remaining flexible will allow you to be ready when baby encounters something new, such as teething and having difficulty falling asleep or eating when he normally would. You will also find that as baby begins to drop naps throughout the day, you will need to adjust his routine. At the time of this writing, my son is eleven months old. It's becoming painfully obvious that he does just fine with one nap. One nap, already? I didn't expect the transition to happen this soon, but I had to be ready to make the adjustment.

It's changing our routine completely—meal times, bottle-feeding, bedtime—but we are adjusting and will find a new groove. Flexibility is key as you walk through baby's first year. His constant changes will rock your world otherwise.

Your Other Job: Encouragement for Working Moms

If you plan to return to work, you are likely making the transition back right about now. Leaving your little one after having months of bonding time will feel very unnatural, perhaps wrong. If God has called you to work in this season of your life, however, there will be great grace upon you to place your child in the care of another. The feelings of sadness and guilt are natural, though, so be kind to yourself as you adjust to this new normal. It will take you a while to get used to your new routine. Seek the support of your spouse and/or family and friends to help you through the first few weeks.

I can remember returning to work after my ten-week maternity leave when my daughter was born. Honestly, part of me was excited to have adult interaction, but overall I was sad to miss any time with my sweet baby. I didn't want to miss a thing. Perhaps this is why I made my mother (her caregiver) write down every little thing she did all day long—when she ate, slept, pooped, and played. I suppose just knowing allowed me some sense of control that I wouldn't otherwise have had being away from her.

Having been a working mom, I can promise you a few things:

1. It will get easier. Give yourself time.
2. It will be good for you. Adult interaction and structure are good for a new mom.
3. You are not ruining your child. If he is in good care (and I'm sure he is if you chose his caregiver), then he will thrive.
4. Your days away from him will only make your nights and weekends home with him sweeter. Savor every moment.
5. You will feel stress. You will feel like you are not giving enough. But grace will cover you.

Both you and your little one are going to be okay. As long as you let your strength come from God and accept his grace in each moment, you will not only be okay, you'll be a wonderful, balanced, thriving, kick-your-dual-role-life-in-the-butt, working mom.

The Life Outside: Encouragement for SAHMs

After the birth of my second child, I had the privilege of being a stay-at-home mom (SAHM). This role comes with a completely different set of challenges I now know—having played both the part of a working mom and, now, a stay-at-home mom. You may not be facing these challenges quite yet, as you are still in the blissful newborn stage with your baby. Eventually, though, you may feel isolated, lonely, and maybe even trapped at home. You may crave adult interaction and structure—especially if you were working before baby arrived.

I'm sure I don't have to convince you that the ability to stay at home with your baby is one of the greatest gifts. Once you find your groove as a mom, there are many ways to deal with the lack you may be feeling.

Here are a few strategies for avoiding the SAHM blues:

1. *Plan your days as much as possible.* Give yourself structure to avoid feeling lack of direction.
2. *Get dressed and put on makeup (even a little bit) every day.*
3. *Find your mom tribe.* Whether it's a mom's group or a girlfriend down the street, find other moms with kids the same age and plan play dates.
4. *Get a hobby.* I know what you are thinking . . . *I just had a baby. How on earth will I find time for a hobby?* Even if it's something you spend a few hours a week on, working on a project will do wonders for your sanity.
5. *Plan "me" time or girl time.* At least once a month (hopefully more), you need time to be by yourself doing grown-up things like shopping, getting a mani/pedi, or having girl's night out.

Stay-at-home moms also need to let their strength come from above. It may meet different needs, but it's still the same grace-filled strength. Ask God to come and guide your days at home. They may seem mundane, but each day with your little one is making valuable deposits into the kingdom of God.

Your Marriage

As your baby experiences constant changes, the relationship between you and your spouse (or support system) may also encounter a natural stress caused by the pressures of this new responsibility, as well as the daily decisions you must make to care for your baby. Before you can hear from God on any issue, you need to be in unity as a family. A very powerful Scripture that encourages peace and unity in the home is found in the book of Colossians. "Let the peace of Christ keep you in tune with each other, in step with each other. None of this going off and doing your own thing. And cultivate thankfulness. Let the Word of Christ—the Message—have the run of the house. Give it plenty of room in your lives. Instruct and direct one another using good common sense. And sing, sing your hearts out to God! Let every detail in your lives—words, actions, whatever—be done in the name of the Master, Jesus, thanking God the Father every step of the way" (Col. 3:15–17 *The Message*). This is the perfect formula for remaining unified and effective in caring for and leading your child. It is also a beautiful design for moving forward in growth in your marriage, despite the stress of a new baby. Your effectiveness as a mother is directly related to your effectiveness as a wife. Do not get so caught up in your new role that you forsake your position as helpmate and partner to your spouse. Although baby's immediate and basic needs will come first, your marriage should always be your top priority.

As you move forward into this season of change and growth, I pray that your constant will be your love for your child and the support you have around you in your spouse or family. God's provision of wisdom and grace is available in abundance. You will abound in every good work, my friend.

Prayer Concerns

Wisdom in the midst of changes

Grace for going back to work

Direction for time at home

My marriage

A Prayer for This Month

Dear Lord,

I thank you for the constant growth I am seeing in my child. It is a testimony to your greatness as I watch my baby develop daily. What a wonderful miracle life is! I ask for your wisdom as we go through what seems like constant changes. Show me what is best for my baby in every moment. Thank you for the grace that is available to me as I operate in the unique role you have called me to as a wife and mother. I desire to be effective in both roles, and I know my ability to do so comes from you. Amen.

Write your own prayer of reflection.

Journal

Finding Pure Joy

Baby Stats

By five months, babies range from 13 to 20 pounds (6–9.2 kg) in weight and approximately 24½ to 27½ inches (62–70 cm) in length.

Development Checker at Five Months

Typical Skills
- ❏ Rolls over one direction
- ❏ Plays with hands and feet
- ❏ Grasps a toy
- ❏ Frequently coos and squeals

Concerning Signs
- ❏ No attempt to roll
- ❏ Minimal smiling or social cues
- ❏ No attempt to make sounds

Language

At about four months, your baby will begin to babble. This is the beginning of his language development. Talking, singing, and reading to your baby are all good ways to encourage language development. You may notice your baby's tone rise and fall. Although it will sound like gibberish to you, he is beginning to form opinions of his own. Spend time making faces and sounds to your baby, and also repeat sounds he makes back to him. He will use these foundational skills to learn to communicate with you.

Movement

Your baby should be getting several periods per day of tummy time by now. His head control has improved dramatically over the past four months, and you'll now see him lift his head off the floor and hold it steady. You can encourage this by lying on the floor with him. Place interesting toys and objects in his view, and talk to him at eye level. He will gradually learn to hold his arms out in front of him and push up with them as well.

Your baby can probably roll over from either front to back or back to front by five months, though there is some variability in age for this skill. Keep thinking about safety at this stage. Remember never to leave your baby unattended on a bed, couch, or changing table, and keep small objects or toys out of his reach.

Discovery. Your four- to five-month-old is all about discovery. At this stage, babies will be awake for longer periods of time, and with not much ability to move yet, they love exploring their limited surroundings. He will start to notice his hands and feet, becoming fascinated by these tools at the end of his limbs. He may lay and stare at them for long periods, probably wondering about all the things he can do with his newfound "toys." Your baby will begin to learn about cause and effect at this age. He may notice that if he shakes or bangs a toy, it makes noise. He will be developmentally mature enough now to try an action again to see if he gets the same reaction. It's an absolute joy to watch your little one discover his surroundings.

By four months of age, he will be able to bring objects to his mouth. Babies love to chew on anything they can get their hands on. Many parents expect that this is a first sign of teething; however, most babies do not get their first tooth until around six months of age. You can probably expect a few more months of chewing and drooling before you reach this milestone.

Social Interaction

You may notice that your baby seems a little fussier during the day at this stage. It is common for a baby to feel frustrated by four to five months of age. As I mentioned earlier, most four- to five-month-olds are awake for longer periods during the day. Your baby is very observant and will want to be right in the middle of whatever activity is going on in the room. If he is unable to sit up and look around, though, he can only get to what is lying right beside him. Your baby will crave constant one-on-one interaction with you and may become fussy if left to lie on his back as you walk away. This is a good time to make more use of infant seats (such as a Bumbo) or a sling that allows baby to remain close to you while you move throughout your day. Sit him in his seat or carry him in a sling so he can watch you as you wash dishes or fold laundry. Talk to him and tell him what you're doing or sing songs. You don't have to be holding him or playing with his toys in order for him to enjoy time with you. You may be tempted to get out the ExerSaucer at this age. While some babies are ready for it now, others are not. Try it out once and see how it goes. If he tips over and can't sit upright in the seat, put it away and try again next month.

Baby Care

Feeding

Starting solid foods. Most babies are ready to eat solid foods somewhere between four and six months of age. The current AAP recommendation is that babies be exclusively breastfed until six months of age ("Switching to Solid Foods," healthychildren.org). At four to five months, your baby may still push against the spoon with his tongue (tongue-thrusting), preventing you from getting any food inside his mouth. If you feel that your child is ready before six months, go ahead and try solids. If you attempt to start baby food at four months and your baby is tongue-thrusting, it is a sign that he is not ready for solids. Wait a few weeks and try again.

For most babies, it doesn't matter what food you feed first. Traditionally, babies are often given rice, oatmeal, or barley cereal first. There is no science to this and no known medical advantage to giving a baby cereal before other foods. Your baby may do very well to skip cereals all together and go right to vegetables and fruits. Newer gastrointestinal studies are finding it may be better to avoid cereals. Talk with your baby's doctor about what foods she would recommend you introduce first. There's also no magic as to what time of day is best to start solids. Pick a time of day when the whole family can be present for this fun, new experience. Remember, the majority of your baby's nutrition still comes from milk. These early solids are simply "practice" foods.

Your baby will probably continue to take the same amount of milk he has been eating even after you start solids. Most babies will not start to "replace" bottles or feedings until a few months from now, often not until they are taking two jars or more of baby food at a time.

The first few meals that your baby eats will probably wind up in his hair and on his clothes (and probably yours, too). Start with just a few teaspoons of food and work up from there. Although many pediatricians will recommend starting vegetables first, there is no strong evidence that your baby will learn to dislike vegetables if you try fruits first. You may choose to buy prepared baby food or make your own. If you do make your own, make sure the consistency is fairly thin at first, then work him toward a yogurt-like consistency by six months.

Once your baby learns to eat one food, gradually give him new foods. Despite what you may have read or heard, a few days between the introduction of each new food is sufficient. It is probably overkill to only do one new food per week. If your baby eats peas for two or three nights in a row and does well, you can move on to the next food. With each new food, look for symptoms of allergic reaction such as rash, diarrhea, or vomiting.

Diapering

You may see some changes in your baby's stools once he begins eating solid foods. This is completely normal, so do not be alarmed when you open up his diaper to reveal a stool of different color, texture, or consistency. Sometimes the changes you see in your baby's bowel movements after starting solid foods are for the better. If your baby tends to be more constipated, start with oatmeal or barley cereal instead of rice cereal. The extra fiber in these cereals can be a God-send for backed-up babies.

Refer to this month's common questions for more information on baby's changing stools.

Sleep and Schedules

At this point, breastfed babies will be eating every three hours during the day with usually one overnight feeding. If you are pumping and giving expressed breast milk, your baby is probably taking 5 to 6 ounces every three hours, while formula-fed babies will be eating 5 to 7 ounces every three to four hours. You may find that as baby sleeps through the night, he wants to cluster feed in the morning to catch up from his long stretch at night. Your baby may also be dropping naps as he begins to sleep more at night, going down to two daytime naps at this age.

Although a typical schedule will still be similar to the examples we gave last month, your baby will be constantly adjusting to new stages, and it may feel as though a schedule is pointless. Teething, eating solid foods, and sleeping longer stretches at night all contribute to how baby moves throughout his day. The best thing you can do is to pay attention to his cues and gently guide him as you remain flexible.

Teething

Teething is highly variable from child to child. In general, you can expect your baby's two front teeth to come in first (either top or bottom). Babies, on average, will get their first tooth at about six months of age. However, the first tooth may erupt anywhere from four months to after his first birthday.

The symptoms of teething are also highly variable between babies. Some babies will have no obvious symptoms at all, and you won't know the tooth is coming until you feel something sharp in his mouth. Other babies will have symptoms preceding tooth eruption. These symptoms may include increased fussiness, loose stools, low-grade fever (around 100 degrees F), drooling, and chewing on objects. Higher fevers of 101 or greater are not typical for teething and are more likely a sign of illness.

Some comfort measures you can take for your baby include massaging his gums with a cool, clean washcloth or using a soft teething ring. Avoid teething rings that freeze solid, as these can actually hurt when baby bites down on them. It is usually not helpful to use topical pain relievers on your baby's gums. These tend to wash off the gums within just a few minutes and don't provide much relief. If you feel that your baby is truly having pain with teething, you may give a weight-appropriate dose of acetaminophen (Tylenol) or use a natural teething relief product such as Hyland's Teething Tablets. Remember, ibuprofen is not approved until six months of age.

Once your baby's tooth comes through, you should clean it every day with a soft cloth or toothbrush and plain water. No toothpaste is needed at this age.

Baby Safety

Baby proofing. At this stage, if you haven't already, you should begin to "baby proof" your home. There are many resources out there in bookstores and on the Internet on effective baby proofing. There are even companies devoted to doing it for you. But baby proofing is not a science. Use common sense. If something would be dangerous for baby to get his little hands on, then remove it, conceal it, or lock it up. Pay close attention to your kitchen, bathroom, laundry room, or utility closet where baby will find breakable items as well as potentially hazardous chemicals. Put baby gates on stairways to keep your soon-to-be crawling little one away from the stairs.

Simple Baby Proofing Checklist

❑ Remove small items (such as toys or trinkets) from baby's reach.

❑ Remove breakable home decor items such as vases or frames.

❑ Install latches on cabinet doors and drawers.

❑ Move all hazardous materials to a high shelf.

❑ Put covers over all accessible outlets.

❑ Conceal electrical cords behind furniture.

❑ Attach corner guards to furniture.

❑ Secure any furniture or lamps that could fall over if baby uses them to pull up.

❑ Keep doors to bathrooms and non-baby-proofed rooms closed.

❑ Install baby gates at the top and bottom of stairs.

Expectations for Your Doctor Visits

There is no scheduled well visit for this month. If your child is behind on any vaccinations, this might be a good time to get caught up.

This is often the age when a baby will get his first minor illness. If you have gone back to work, your baby may be in day care now. Though day care centers try their best to keep things clean and free of illness, it is just inevitable that illness will spread in these active, social environments. There's nothing that kids share better than germs.

Baby's first illness is often very alarming to new parents. After all, no one likes to see their baby feeling poorly or in pain, especially when he is still so small. Most of the time, these illnesses are very minor and are easily treated with either time and supportive care or medications. If your baby has a fever greater than 101 degrees for more than just a few days, he should be evaluated by his pediatrician to make sure that there is nothing more serious going on. You will find more information about baby's first illnesses in Month Four and Month Six.

Behind the Scenes of Your Pediatrician's Office

While some pediatric practices are able to answer all calls as they come in, it is possible that you will need to leave a message when you call your child's doctor. Most calls made by parents take several minutes each, since the parent usually needs to describe symptoms and get advice or make an appointment. Since more than one call may be coming in at the same time, your call may go to a nurse's voicemail, and you'll wait for a call back. It is reasonable to expect that most calls will be answered the same day.

There are a few tips for getting your calls answered in a timely manner. When leaving a message, be sure to include your child's name and date of birth. Speak clearly and say on the message exactly what you need so that the appropriate person will call back (e.g., my child needs a six-month checkup; my child needs a referral to see a dermatologist; or my child has a fever and a runny nose.) Most importantly, make sure to clearly leave a number that you will be able to answer when you are called back. Do not assume that the office already has your contact information—leave your number every time. If your cell phone voicemail is not set up or is full, if you may have limited minutes left on your phone, or if you are unable to answer your cell phone at work, that may not be the best number to leave for a call back. Following these tips will help with a timely call back and aid your child's doctor in getting your needs met.

Remember that there are dozens of mothers calling your doctor's office every single day. While your pediatrician and her staff desire to meet everyone's needs in a timely manner, there are only so many minutes in a day. You can help by being thorough and considerate of their time and working together in partnership with them to care for your child.

Common Questions You May Have This Month

What can I expect after my baby starts solid foods?

After your baby starts solids, the first change you will notice is a difference in his stools. They will usually be more firm in consistency. Particularly if you have been exclusively breastfeeding, you may notice that his stools are much more solid. (Conversely, if your baby has been formula-fed and has had constipation issues, you may see that solid foods help to soften stools.) He may have more or less than he did before. His stools will become more variable in color (green after eating peas and red after eating beets, for example). Because of the introduction of new fats and sugars in these foods, they will also become much stronger in odor. Starchy foods tend to cause more solid stools, so make sure you give a good variety if you notice symptoms of constipation. If you make your baby's food or if it is not strained, you may notice undigested food in his stools. This is very normal and not a cause for concern.

Babies' digestive systems are unfamiliar with processing new foods and may take some time to adjust. If your baby's stools are extremely watery or full of mucus, reduce the amount of solids you are giving. You may need to introduce them more slowly. If the symptoms persist, call his doctor for further recommendations.

My baby is not yet rolling over. Should I be concerned?

Not necessarily. By four to five months, babies should at least be *attempting* to roll over. Your baby may only be able to get to his side before getting stuck. Give him some time—he'll figure it out. Babies who are long and lean tend to develop this skill sooner than babies with bigger bellies and chubbier legs. If your baby is five months old and is not even attempting to roll over, this is of more concern, and you should inform your pediatrician. She may want to refer your child to a physical therapist or a developmental practitioner for a more thorough evaluation.

My baby is still not on a feeding schedule. Is that okay?

It's okay from a developmental standpoint, though it may be frustrating to some families. While it may be more convenient for a baby to be on a very strict and predictable four-hour feeding schedule, it is often not possible. Remember, just because you read a method book doesn't mean your baby has read the book and will comply. Learn to relax a little and go with the flow. There are a lot of changes on the horizon, including starting solids, teething, and changing nap schedules. These will all mess up a previously planned-out schedule. Your baby may simply be hungrier one day than another, which is also normal. If he is resistant to a schedule, simply follow his cues. Chances are, he'll eventually fall into a rhythm on his own with your gentle guidance.

A Real-Life Story

A Child with Special Needs

Elizabeth, mom to Owen, Lukas, Avery, and Eliot

"It isn't our job to understand, anticipate or even know what God is doing. Instead, we are to abide in Him through everything that comes our way. As you worship God this morning at church try to just enjoy Him and rest in His presence rather than strive for an answer. He has got you in the palm of His hand."

I texted these words to my friend from a deeply authentic place in my heart it could not have come from a year prior. Our world had changed dramatically with the birth of our fourth child. Once again, God had an unexpected way of interlacing truth deep within our being to form us in the likeness of his purpose.

In the summer of 2011, our Eliot Jace entered the world. The team delivering him immediately noticed something was wrong. It was not long before we learned Eliot had a 9 by 6 centimeter cyst in the center of his brain and a condition called hydrocephalus.

Medically speaking, we were told his condition had no cure. Hydrocephalus becomes fatal if not treated effectively. This awful condition also exposes its victim to an ongoing risk of brain damage. Babies born with hydrocephalus face a lifetime of brain surgeries that come with little warning. Facing this reality while we had expected yet another perfectly healthy child was an incredible shift.

I had grown up reading through passages like Matthew 6:25–34 (do not worry) and Romans 8:28 (be anxious for nothing). They often left me begging God to make me more like the truths they contained. So, what was God thinking giving this sweet, precious boy to a mom who has had anxiety-centered labels slapped on her throughout her entire life? He had to know how incapable I was! Surely he meant to give this situation to some woman who sweats nothing, runs the perfect house, and has a large, glow-in-the-dark "S" painted on her chest. The woman who is written about in Proverbs 31, whose children "rise and call her blessed."

BUT.

God's ways are not our ways; his thoughts are not our thoughts. The Truth says that when Father God sees me, he sees the woman he created me to be, redeemed and without blemish. His purpose weaves deep into my DNA and becomes perfected by his Spirit. While the Devil has meant to harm us, God has intended this to strengthen us instead. He has set us free.

In addition to the incredible growth of our spiritual understanding throughout this past year, we have learned important qualities to help us manage our new reality. If you have been given the blessing of a child with special needs, here are a few tips from what we have learned on our journey thus far.

Be prepared. I try to keep an overnight bag packed with comfortable clothes, pajamas, toiletries, and snacks with a long shelf life since we might be in the ER for long periods of time without even a break to get to a vending machine. We have an envelope that comes with us if we travel far away from Eliot's hospital. It contains Eliot's MRIs and a sheet with all his doctors' information, surgery dates, insurance information, and medical equipment serial numbers. We don't leave town without these things in case we have an emergency away from our home hospital.

Be flexible. We have had to learn to take the concept "take things as they come" to a deeper level. When Eliot was in a time of back-to-back surgeries, we moved his crib into our room. After surgeries, he often needs a period of time where he sleeps with his head elevated. At times, this meant a Nap Nanny; at other times, it meant getting creative with his crib settings. We find ourselves problem solving a lot to adjust to the reality we are facing that moment. You may need to let go of your desire to do it "perfectly," because what's best for your child will look much different than it does for others.

Trust God. Most importantly, we trust God. In his first year, Eliot has had eight brain surgeries. If I had known about these circumstances ahead of time, I would have surely lost the air from my lungs and melted straight into the floor. I did not and do not need to know. I've learned I only need to grasp that whatever happens in my life, God has me. He has Eliot. He has my husband. He has my other three beautiful children. Whatever we walk through, God has more than we need. And that is more than enough.

Truth for the Journey

"The Lord is my strength and my shield; my heart trusts in him, and he helps me. My heart leaps for joy, and with my song I praise him." Psalm 28:7

My little guy (eleven months old at the time of this writing) has been a complete joy since the day he was born. That doesn't mean it hasn't been hard. Life with a baby is just challenging in many respects. But his almost constant smile, the new things he does and discovers daily, and the fact that his life is a complete miracle ordained by

God for such a time as this are some of these things that bring me pure joy. I want this joy for you, too, sweet mama.

I'm not sure I experienced as much of this joy after my daughter was born. That has nothing to do with her and everything to do with the fact that I was intimidated by my first baby. There were days I was scared stiff of what she might do or not do. I had fun with her, but I'm afraid I missed out on a lot of enjoyment because it was overshadowed by fear. Fear of failing. Fear of being out of control.

As you move past the shock season where you've had to adjust your entire life for your baby, I hope to encourage you to settle in and enjoy your little one. Things aren't perfect, and they will never be. As soon as you get him on a schedule, your baby will start teething and wake up in the middle of the night. As soon as you get past that stage, he'll move to one nap, and you'll adjust again. Don't wait for things to settle down or get easier before you enjoy your child. Find joy in every moment—whether you are sleep-deprived or well-rested, pooped on or freshly showered.

Our key verse for this month is from Psalm 28. I love how David goes back and forth in this book of songs—from sharing his plight to shouting sure praises. We mamas often feel the same way as we move through challenging yet exciting seasons with baby. David is not afraid to call out to the Lord in distress, but at the end of the day—in this as well as many other Psalms—David is able to proclaim, "The Lord is my strength and my shield; my heart trusts in him, and he helps me. My heart leaps for joy, and with my song I praise him." Don't you want that to be your heart? I know I do. I want to be able to say, "Help me, Lord! I trust you because you are good and you care about these mundane mommy days. I will shout for joy in the midst of the chaos because you have blessed me with the life of my child. I praise you in the midst of this mess because you are my help and my strength." Let go of your fears, my friend, and embrace the fun and enjoyment that come with a new life whose eyes are opening to the world around him. Find pure and unabashed joy in every moment of your days. They will fly by, and you won't remember the sleepless nights, but you will remember his first smile, his first roll, the first time he stuck his sweet little toes in his mouth. Let the joy of those moments carry you.

Ways to Soak Up the Joyful Moments

- Forget about the dishes. Leave them in the sink and get down on the floor with your baby.
- Try to discover what games make your baby giggle most. Play them daily.
- What book is your baby most interested in? Read it every day and watch the joy he gets from his favorite story.
- Find his tickle spots. Baby giggles are, by far, the best sound in the world.
- Sing to him and find the song he reacts to most. He'll likely have a favorite after hearing it several times.

Making Your Own Baby Food

Dr. Johnston shared this month about starting solid foods. You may decide to make your own baby food in order to save money or to give your child more natural, organic foods. Whether you choose to feed your baby food from a jar you purchased at the grocery store or from a container you filled yourself—there is no right or wrong. But, if you feel passionate about making your own food, then by all means go for it.

There are several reasons to make your own baby food:

1. It's economical (when you plan).
2. You know exactly what's in baby's food.
3. You can get your baby used to eating what you eat.
4. You can create the texture you feel your baby is ready for.
5. It creates less waste. No empty jars or containers.

There is nothing wrong with feeding your baby food from a jar (or a pouch, these days). There are many options on the market that are perfectly healthy for baby, including many organic options. But if you are interested in trying your hand at making baby food, here are a few tips to get you started.

Shop

Buy the freshest produce possible and use items within a day or two after purchase. Choose vegetables that are not high in nitrates, which can be harmful to baby. Those known to have high nitrate levels are: green beans, carrots, spinach, squash, and beets. It is not a bad idea to use frozen vegetables to prepare baby food, especially if you want to try the items listed above. The AAP recommends peas, corn, and sweet potatoes as good first foods for babies.

Steam and Smash

When making baby food, find a system that works well for your schedule and your available storage. You will need to have a good system of food preparation if you want to be in this for the long haul. Choose a day of the week where you can set aside an hour or two for baby food prep. Sunday afternoons are a great time for this.

Thoroughly wash your fruits and vegetables using a brush. There are many ways to prepare each food, but generally you will need to cut or peel your fruits and vegetables to start. Specifically, for a younger baby, be careful you don't leave too much skin on. Although there is lots of nutrition in the skin, it will add to the bulk and texture of prepared foods and can be harmful to baby. Once baby is older and can handle more texture, you can leave more of the nutritious skins on.

Next, you'll steam or boil the food to get it nice and soft. Make sure it is cooked through enough to be pureed to your baby's preference. Last, you'll run your cooked fruits and veggies through a food processor. There are several baby food making systems on the market today that do this quite easily. But a good ole kitchen food processor or blender works just fine as well. Once again, be sure that the food is pureed enough and is the texture you are comfortable with for your baby's stage. You will find a list of our recommended baby food making products and resources in the Appendix.

Store

Several of the baby food making systems today come with convenient storage tools. An old-fashioned ice cube tray (remember those?) or small, disposable bowls with lids work fine as well. Divide your pureed food into equal parts (an ice cube is the perfect serving size), cover well to avoid freezer burn, and label with food name and date. (Some items will alter in color after freezing, so it will help to have them labeled.) The key is to store food in serving sizes so you can easily remove a serving from the freezer to give to baby each day.

Serve

Remove the portion of baby food you want to use from the freezer prior to serving. Allow enough time for the food to thaw. It may be helpful to take a day's worth of food out of the freezer and keep it in the fridge. If you heat the food in the microwave, be sure to check thoroughly for hot pockets to avoid burning baby's mouth. Consider sectioning out even one serving into two in case your baby does not want an entire ice cube-sized portion. You should dispose of any unused food that baby's spoon has touched, so in order to avoid waste, use a separate bowl or dish to feed baby from.

Managing Everyday Tasks

You may be overwhelmed by managing your everyday, normal household tasks, let alone the idea of making your own baby food. Remember that your most important task every day is to love on your baby and soak up every moment of your time with him. But still, the laundry needs to get done and dinner won't cook itself. Try to prioritize your tasks at the beginning of every week. Make a list of what needs to get done and tackle those tasks one at a time. You may only get dinner made and one load of laundry washed and folded per day. I'm here to tell you, those accomplishments deserve an award for any new mama!

As your baby falls into a more predictable routine, so will you. In the meantime, be kind to yourself. Make sure your expectations are in line with what you are able to do now, not based on what you did before you had a baby. When you master your ability to cook a meal, do a load or two of laundry, and vacuum a room each day while still enjoying time with your baby, you can think about including additional tasks in your day.

As you let the joy of your baby carry you through these months, mama, invite God into every moment and allow your communion with him to deepen your trust. Your joy will lead to a heart of thanksgiving, and greater trust will deepen your faith. Gratitude and faith are the perfect ingredients for a peace-filled journey of motherhood.

Prayer Concerns

Pure joy

Transition to solid food

Deeper trust

A Prayer for This Month

Dear Lord,

What joy it is to be a mom. Even in the midst of the craziness, I ask that you help me to stop and soak up the joyful moments. Don't let me miss them, Lord. Thank you for the smiles that make my heart leap and the daily developments that let me know your hand is on me and my baby. I desire to deepen my trust in you daily, Father, as I grow as a mom. Guide us with your constant and gentle hand. Amen.

Write your own prayer of reflection.

_____

_____

_____

_____

Journal

_____

_____

_____

_____

_____

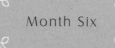

The Halfway Mark

Baby Stats

By six months, babies range from 14 to 21 pounds (6.4–9.6 kg) in weight and approximately 25 to 28 inches (64–72 cm) in length.

Development Checker at Six Months

Typical Skills

- ❏ Rolls over both directions
- ❏ Turns toward sounds and voices
- ❏ Recognizes familiar faces
- ❏ Sits with minimal support
- ❏ Stands and bounces when held up

Concerning Signs

- ❏ Head still flops back when pulled from lying on back to a seated position
- ❏ No attempt to bear weight on legs

Language

At six months, your baby should be able to laugh aloud, babble, and squeal. He may be able to make consonant sounds ("b" and "d" are often first) while he is babbling. You might notice that he likes hearing the sound of his voice. He may make sounds as a means to keep himself awake if he is trying to avoid naptime. Continue to talk to your baby using fun and bright expressions. The smiles he returns will be more than enough to carry you through your busy days, mom.

Movement

Your baby should be able to lie on his belly and push up with his arms and arch his back to lift his chest up off the floor. You may also notice him lying on his belly and kicking his legs and arms like he is swimming. This is the first stage in preparing to crawl. He should be able to roll over in both directions (belly to back and back to belly) by now. He may also begin to scoot or creep when lying on his belly as he begins to practice crawling movements. Keep giving him daily play time on the floor. Get down on the floor with him and encourage him to reach for toys and your face. He will love the one-on-one attention, and it will be good exercise for him, too. This is especially true for a baby that "hates tummy time." It's a good idea to get down on the floor with your baby and interact with him so he will learn to enjoy it.

Pushing up on his arms and lifting his chest off the floor is a sign that he is gaining not only arm strength but also strength in his trunk. This is a good time to help him practice sitting up. Sit with him and gently hold him steady, or prop him up on the couch or floor with pillows. This will continue to help him strengthen his upper body and learn to sit up on his own. While he may be able to tripod somewhat (placing his hands on the floor to steady himself while sitting), he will still tip over easily at this point and needs close supervision when sitting alone.

When lying on his back, your baby may pull his feet to his mouth. Before long, he'll be sucking on his toes daily. This is part of his discovery process as he becomes familiar with his flexibility and body parts. You may notice that he is discovering other body parts as well. He may start batting at his ears. This can be confusing to parents (and doctors) because babies also touch their ears to indicate pain when they have an ear infection. They may also touch them from referred pain to the ears caused by teething. If you have any concerns, have him checked out by his pediatrician to verify that nothing is wrong. Consider it a relief if the doctor tells you that, in fact, there is no infection and he has simply "found" his ears!

When held in a standing position, your baby can bear weight on his legs and may bounce up and down. Now may be a good time to get out the ExerSaucer and see if he can sit well enough to keep upright and play with the toys. These stationary play saucers are a great tool to keep baby occupied long enough to get dinner on the table.

Baby can hold an object in his hands and even transfer it from one hand to the other. Give him toys that jingle and shake to help him learn cause and effect.

Social Interaction

At this stage, your baby is starting to recognize familiar faces. This will be extremely rewarding for mommy, daddy, and grandparents as they begin to receive a warm welcome from baby. While true "separation anxiety" may not come for a few more months, your baby may react more strongly to his primary caregiver because he knows your face.

Baby Care

Feeding

The primary source of your baby's nutrition is still breast milk or formula. Most six-month-olds drink between 24 and 36 ounces per day. If your baby is getting less than 33 ounces of formula per day, he still needs a vitamin D supplement. You may just now be starting baby food, particularly if your baby was exclusively breastfeeding. See Month Four and Month Five for more details on starting solids. If your baby has already started solids, he may be ready for Stage 2 foods at this age.

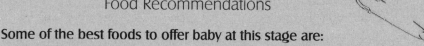

Food Recommendations

Some of the best foods to offer baby at this stage are:
Stage 1 and 2 baby foods
Yogurt (you don't have to buy baby yogurt, the adult kind is fine)
Bites of avocado
Mashed-up banana
Hummus

Foods to avoid:
Any choking hazards (hard pieces of food, large bites of food, sticky textures)
Honey
Extra salt or seasoning added to their foods. Their little palates are used to bland foods, so it's best not to overwhelm them with rich seasoning at this time.

Babies receive an adequate amount of water from breast milk or formula. However, if you would like to give your baby sips of water on a hot day, it is fine at this stage. A common question that moms will ask is how much juice their baby needs each day. Juice is not "needed" at all. No matter if the label says "100% juice" or not, doctors and nutritionists agree that juices for children are mainly just sugar water—empty calories with little nutritional benefit. If you do decide to offer your baby juice, it should be diluted and no more than 4 ounces per day. Exceptions to this rule are babies who have constipation issues and may benefit from daily prune juice or white grape juice.

("The Use and Misuse of Fruit Juice in Pediatrics," AAP, pediatrics.aappublications.org.)

Teething

Your baby will get his first teeth in the coming months. Six months of age is typical to see the first tooth come through—usually on the bottom center of the gum. Watch for him to have increased drooling and fussiness just before these teeth come in. You will need to care for his teeth as soon as they begin to appear. Get in the habit of brushing his teeth after meals and at bedtime as soon as his first tooth is visible. You can wipe off the teeth with a clean, wet washcloth or use a soft baby toothbrush and water. You do not need to use any toothpaste on his teeth. Fluoridated toothpastes may lead to a permanent discoloration of baby's teeth.

Sleep and Schedules

Most six-month-olds still need two naps per day and will be cranky if a nap is missed. Continue to have consistent routines at bedtime and naptime. Starting at about six to nine months of age, your child may begin to develop some separation anxiety during naps and overnight. This is a very common occurrence, even in babies that previously slept well through the night. Your child may wake several times and cry out for you. Keep his routines consistent and reassure him that you are close by. You may need to go into his room and give him a pacifier or other security object, but do not start habits such as letting him fall asleep in your bed or on the couch, then moving him into his bed. This will only make his anxiety worse when he wakes up and realizes he's not in the same place. The only way to ensure he will learn to soothe himself back to sleep is to keep the sleep environment consistent.

Baby Safety

Sun exposure. Keep baby in the shade as much as possible. Have him always wear a hat with a wide brim to protect his scalp and shade his face, ears, and neck from direct sunlight. Choose lightweight clothing with a tight weave to filter more sunlight. It is okay to apply sunscreen to exposed areas of baby's skin, such as the face and top of the hands and arms. As we mentioned earlier in the book, choose a sunscreen that says "broad-spectrum" and protects against UVA and UVB rays. The higher a sunscreen's SPF (sun protection factor), the better the coverage against UV rays. You should always choose a sunscreen of SPF 30 or higher. Because he is able to move around now and may find himself in different positions with sun exposure, use enough sunscreen to cover baby's entire body from head to toes. Sunscreen should be applied twenty to thirty minutes prior to going outdoors in order to be most beneficial. Reapply sunscreen every two hours, as it will wear off from swimming, sweating, or just soaking into the skin.

Remember, just because your baby can wear sunscreen does not mean you should have him out in the heat of summer for extended periods of time. Avoid the peak hours of sunlight exposure from 10:00 A.M. to 4:00 P.M. whenever possible. Make a habit of applying sunscreen anytime you will be outdoors.

Illness

Depending on the time of year your baby is born, he will be exposed to a variety of illnesses in the first six months of life. Some of the more common childhood illnesses include the following list.

Thrush. *Candida* fungus is normally found in small amounts on the skin. However, especially in babies, this fungus can overgrow and cause thrush in the mouth. This might occur during the newborn period as baby's immune system is developing or later in infancy after antibiotic use. Thrush symptoms include white patches on the lips, tongue, palate, and inside of cheeks. Sometimes it can be difficult to determine if the white patches on a baby's tongue are thrush or just milk staining. Your doctor may take a wooden tongue depressor and try to gently scrape your baby's tongue. Milk will come off and thrush will not. Thrush can be painful, and babies sometimes will not want to nurse or bottle-feed as much until it is healed. Your child's pediatrician will typically prescribe an oral antifungal medication to be given for two weeks. Your doctor will probably ask you to sterilize all baby's bottles and pacifiers until the thrush is gone. If you are breastfeeding, you may need to be treated as well. Refer back to our discussion on thrush in Month One and ask your OB for her recommendations.

Common cold. An upper respiratory infection (URI), or common cold, is probably the most common illness your baby will have in the first year of life. URIs are caused by numerous different viruses that are spread easily through contact with an ill person who is coughing or sneezing. Especially for children in day care, the common cold will almost certainly occur in the first year of life. Common colds typically start with a fever and peak at around three to five days. Your baby may have fever, cough, and nasal symptoms. Nasal drainage typically starts out clear but may become cloudy, yellow, or green after the first few days of illness. A color change in his nasal drainage does not necessarily mean he has a sinus infection or needs an antibiotic. This nasal drainage will typically transition back to clear as the virus goes away. Common colds can last anywhere from one to two weeks.

While there are no prescription medications that can make a URI go away more quickly, there are some things you can do at home to make your child more comfortable. Run a cool mist humidifier in his room at night to moisten the air. Make sure it is cleaned regularly according to the manufacturer's recommendations. Nasal saline drops or spray may be used in your child's nose to break up nasal secretions prior to bulb suctioning. You may also want to elevate the head of your baby's bed so that he will be slightly inclined when sleeping.

If your child has been sick for more than one week, or seems to be getting worse instead of better after a few days, he should be evaluated by his doctor.

Croup. Croup is a viral infection that is common in children under three years of age. Croup causes swelling and inflammation of the voice box (larynx) and windpipe (trachea), resulting in a characteristic hoarse, "barking" cough. Croup may seem like a minor common cold at first, but after a few days, a seal-like barking cough will appear, often at night. For mild cases of croup, take your baby into a steamy bathroom or outside into cool night air to help alleviate the cough. Although croup is usually a minor illness, the swelling of the windpipe can become severe in a minority of patients. If your child seems to have difficulty breathing or is becoming overly tired or upset from rapid breathing, he should be seen in an emergency room as soon as possible. Often a simple breathing treatment specially given in hospitals and a dose of steroid will relieve the worst symptoms.

Ear infection. Ear infections are also a common source of illness in children. Children in day cares and children who are exposed to cigarette smoke seem to be particularly vulnerable. Ear infections are one of the most frustrating diagnoses for parents to figure out. Most moms worry that if their child is especially fussy or running a fever, then there must be an ear infection. There is good reason to be concerned! Babies can't talk, after all, and it's difficult to know why your baby is irritable. Maybe it's sore ears, maybe it's teething pain, maybe it's a tummy ache. If you suspect that your baby has an ear infection, he should be seen by his pediatrician. She can take a quick look and help figure out what is wrong. It may just be a false alarm, and that's okay. Pediatricians *love* false alarms—we don't want your baby to be in pain! It's no problem at all just to take a look.

If your baby has more than just a few ear infections in the first year, your doctor might recommend that he be seen by an otolaryngologist (ENT) to discuss ear tubes. Constant ear infections can lead to damage to the eardrum, hearing loss, and speech delay, so it's important to keep a close eye if your child has several infections.

Bronchiolitis. Bronchiolitis is a viral respiratory infection typically seen in the winter months. Although many viruses can cause bronchiolitis, the most well-known is respiratory syncytial virus (RSV). Babies who are born prematurely are especially susceptible to RSV and may even receive a special monthly vaccine to prevent this illness during peak months. The primary symptoms of RSV are fever, nasal congestion, cough, and wheezing. While there is no specific treatment to make bronchiolitis go away faster, there are comfort measures you can use to make your child feel better until the illness passes. Nasal saline and a room humidifier are especially important for clearing the nasal passages during RSV. Elevate your baby's head while he is sleeping. Be sure to watch for any signs of respiratory distress, and call your doctor right away if you are concerned. Unlike a regular cold that might last seven days or so, RSV tends to linger. Symptoms generally peak by the end of the first week and slowly resolve over the next two to four weeks.

Hand, foot, and mouth disease. Hand, foot, and mouth disease is a common illness seen in infants and young children. It is caused by a virus and is diagnosed by symptoms and physical exam. There are no tests typically done to diagnose hand, foot, and mouth disease. Symptoms include fever, fussiness, and small sores or blisters in the mouth and throat, hands, and feet. The diaper area may be affected as well. Symptoms generally last one week and go away gradually on their own. There is no treatment to make this virus go away more quickly. You may give your child acetaminophen or ibuprofen for fever and pain relief. The main cause for concern with hand, foot, and mouth disease is potential dehydration. Sometimes children with this illness have so many blisters in their throat that they refuse to drink due to pain. If your child has a dry mouth or not enough wet diapers, you should call his doctor right away.

Using medication. Acetaminophen (Tylenol) is the only pain reliever approved for infants under six months of age. Once your baby is six months old, ibuprofen (Motrin or Advil) can be used. Be sure to check with your doctor for the correct dosage for your baby's size.

There are no over-the-counter cough and cold medications currently approved for use during the first year of life.

Using a bulb syringe. Despite the many options you will find at your local superstore, ask any mom and she'll tell you the only bulb syringe that actually works is the one they give you in the hospital. Hopefully you've kept it on hand and snagged another. When you hear your baby struggling to breathe when he is sick, you will want to do anything to relieve his discomfort. Bulb syringes are a great tool to clear baby's passages. It is important to remember, though, that you can only expect to suck out something you can *see* in baby's nose. Much of what you *hear* cannot be removed by suction. Use a nasal saline spray, and then attempt to suction baby's nose once. If you do not retrieve any snot, then leave it alone. Any further attempts will only irritate or inflame baby's passages, making it that much harder for him to breathe. Your baby will probably not like having something stuck up his nose. If you can, recruit your spouse or a family member to hold baby or distract him while you use the bulb syringe.

Expectations for Your Doctor Visits

Your child will receive his third dose of several routine vaccines at this month's visit. According to the AAP recommended vaccination schedule, he should receive a liquid rotavirus vaccine and several injections. The shots will include boosters to DTaP, polio, Hib, hepatitis B, and pneumococcus. Some of these may be offered as a combination vaccine. Check with your doctor ahead of time to find out what she has scheduled for your baby so you can be prepared. You can expect a low-grade fever and mild, local tenderness at the site of the injection, just like the last time. Your baby's pediatrician will also review his growth and development with you at this visit. Your baby should be making great progress on his social and motor skills by the six-month checkup, so be prepared to ask any questions about concerns you may have.

A flu shot is recommended during flu season for infants six months of age or older. Though the flu can occur any time of year, the typical flu season is between October and May, with a peak around January or February. Many pediatricians will start giving flu vaccines as early as August or September. Some parents worry that by giving the vaccine too early in the fall, it might not "last" all the way through flu season. This is not the case, however, and vaccinating early will help prevent the illness when flu season comes a little sooner. The flu vaccine needs approximately two weeks to take effect, and protection lasts for at least one year. Getting vaccinated in December or even later in the flu season can still be beneficial.

The flu vaccine is recommended for all children six months and older. If your child is younger than six months during flu season, the rest of the family and caregivers should receive the vaccine for baby's protection. I often stress the importance of the vaccine even more for parents that work with the public, especially health-care workers, teachers, and those in the service industry who are exposed to people coming and going every day.

Common Questions You May Have

How can I tell if my baby has an ear infection?

Ear infections seem to plague some babies. It seems like every time you turn around, your child is back in the office with another infection. Some babies manage to get through the first year without a single infection, though this is rare. The most common reason moms bring baby in for an ear check is that he is batting at or pulling on his ear. For some babies, this is a tell-tale sign and nearly always accurate. Other babies will have these same reactions to teething pain, to being sleepy, or just out of boredom or habit. Some babies always run a fever with their ear infections, while others never do. The bottom line is, while symptoms of ear infection may be elusive, it is the easiest thing to check and diagnose. It's worth a trip to the pediatrician just to be sure.

I think my baby is sick, but I feel stupid taking him to the doctor again. . . .

First of all, *stop* any thoughts of feeling "stupid." It is never stupid to take your child back to his doctor if you think there is something wrong. I'll often have moms bring in their children for a runny nose and cough from the previous day or two. I'll listen to their lungs and look at their ears and all seems well except for a simple upper respiratory infection—just a "cold." Most of the time, these children get better in four or five days and have no issues. Sometimes these simple viral infections can worsen into more serious issues such as severe ear infections or even pneumonia. I encourage parents to give viral illnesses a few days, but if things don't seem better and definitely if your child is getting worse, you should bring baby back in for another check.

This is probably a good opportunity to discuss the benefit of seeing your child's personal doctor versus frequent visits to various "quick" clinics around town. I'll admit it—they sure are convenient for parents, and they are often open later in the evening when your child's regular doctor's office may be closed. Unfortunately, most of these quick clinics and minor emergency centers are staffed by adult-trained, mid-level providers and doctors with no pediatrics background. Particularly if you think your child has something more than a simple cold, it is better to have him seen by his own doctor, who knows him and you and can offer an accurate pediatric perspective.

Mommy Care

Postpartum Anxiety

All moms worry about the health and safety of their little ones, but for some the worry begins to overwhelm their life, developing into postpartum anxiety disorder. Postpartum anxiety disorder is suspected when you are constantly thinking of fearful things that might happen to you or your baby. Anxiety may also come from being overwhelmed or feelings of failure or frustration. Your worry and fear can result in symptoms of irritability, fatigue, loss of concentration, sweating, nausea, diarrhea, exaggerated startle response, or insomnia.

Full-blown panic attacks can also occur. Panic attacks are instances where you feel short of breath, chest pain, and a sense of impending doom. These often bring women to the hospital thinking they are having a heart attack.

Anxiety and panic disorders can be treated with therapy or medications similar to those that treat PPD. If you think you may be experiencing postpartum anxiety, discuss your concerns with your OB.

Truth for the Journey

"Blessed are those whose strength is in you, whose hearts are set on the pilgrimage. They go from strength to strength, till each appears before God in Zion."

Psalm 84:5, 7

This month, you hit the halfway mark of baby's first year! I'm sure you feel as though time is flying by. It's true what they say . . . with kids, the days are long but the years are short.

Our key verse for this month spoke volumes to me as I read and studied it. Especially as it pertains to motherhood and parenting. When we set our hearts on the journey, we go from strength to strength, day by day. That strength can only be found in the God of heaven. What a powerful promise—a promise built on the idea of seeing our days as a pilgrimage. The thing about a pilgrimage or a journey is that it's not short. We are in this for the long haul, mama, and as you turn the corner of year one, I want to encourage you to set your heart on the journey and find your strength in him.

Viewing your days as a pilgrimage will keep you from getting caught up in the mundane and help you focus on the big picture. With all of the decisions you have to make as a baby mama, it's easy to overthink every little thing and get bogged down in the details. Your baby's first year will be over with the blink of an eye. True, there are many foundational issues such as eating, sleep habits, and health that will follow you into the next season, but don't let your mind be consumed by those decisions. Set your heart on the journey and watch God lead you day by day, from strength to strength. This promise will follow you into every season of your child's life. What a privilege that we do not travel alone.

As your baby begins to laugh and babble, and as he starts to recognize your face more, you will feel a different bond with him. It is so rewarding to be responded to and to receive a precious grin from your baby. Enjoy this new stage and let the joy carry you through the tough moments.

It will also be fun to play games with your baby now that he can interact more. Focus on activities that encourage interaction, language, and mobility. Remember to celebrate baby's accomplishments with an enthusiastic "Yay!" or hand clap.

Fun Games to Play with Baby at Six Months

1. *Peekaboo* – He may not catch on right away, but playing this classic game of hide-and-seek will become a favorite.

2. *What does a "cow" say?* – Basic animal sounds are similar to baby's first babbles, so he will be able to repeat them back to you with some practice.

3. *Where are baby's nose and toes?* – Point out certain body parts and teach baby to recognize them.

4. *Toy grasp* – Put a few of his favorite toys just slightly out of reach and watch him work on his mobility while trying to grasp them.

Shopping for Baby

Shopping for your baby is such a fun part of being a mom. We are definitely not without options these days, as store after store is stocked full of adorable outfits and accessories. It's easy to get carried away. As a planner, one lesson I learned the hard way is to not buy too much ahead of time for baby. As I mentioned in Month Two when we discussed shopping and baby's needs, your little one is growing at a rapid pace during the first year. It is hard to know what size he will be wearing next month, let alone in six months. If you are like me and love to snag end-of-season clearance deals, consider these tips when shopping ahead for baby.

Consider buying a size up. If your baby will be 18 months old a year from your end-of-season clearance spree, look at 24-month clothes. Chances are he can get away with a slightly larger size, whereas after a growth spurt, his true size may be a tad too small.

Look for bottoms with adjustable waists. This clever invention has been a lifesaver for me. Adjustable waist bottoms have an inner elastic band that can be cinched to adjust the size. This way you can buy a size up without worrying about his pants falling down.

Stick with the basics. If you are buying a size up and stick with basics, you'll eventually get to use them. T-shirts, jeans, bodysuits, light sweaters, and dresses are all items that can be layered and used across seasons.

Buy only one signature outfit. You know the one . . . it's the perfectly adorable outfit that costs way too much, but since it's on clearance you can justify it? Yeah, that one. I'm always tempted to buy two or three of these on sale, but if you are buying in advance, it's best not to go crazy. (I'm preaching to myself here, too.)

If you don't get caught up in clearance sales like the rest of us and prefer to buy your baby's wardrobe in real-time, there are several tricks to remember. Although you may not want to wait for deep discounts and shop a whole year ahead, you can find initial clearance sales if you wait just a tad into the current season. Shop for fall in October, winter in January, spring in April, and summer in July.

Don't forget to look for coupons and general sales. Sign up for your favorite store's e-mail list. Most stores can scan coupons directly off your smartphone now, which eliminates the need to print them out. Check out apps such as RetailMeNot and CouponCabin so you can access coupons anytime, anywhere.

As I mentioned back in Month Two, don't forget to look for consignment sales in your area. These sales are a mecca for gently used children's clothing, toys, and gear. Especially in the first year when baby moves through these items so quickly, it is easy to find toys and gear in great shape that have barely been used by their previous owners.

I hope you can set your mind on the long haul, but I don't want you to get carried away and miss out on the delight of each day with your baby. Ask the Lord for balance in living in the moment while setting your heart on the pilgrimage. He will meet you daily with the grace you need for the now and the not yet.

Prayer Concerns

Baby's language and mobile development
Protection against illness
Eyes to see the pilgrimage
Grace for each day

A Prayer for This Month

Dear Lord,
Thank you that we are not alone on this pilgrimage of parenting. Help me to
set my heart on the journey, God. I long to achieve balance in living each day

fully while looking toward all you have for us in the coming seasons. Protect
my baby from illnesses that he may be exposed to. I trust you will cover his
body with your precious blood. As we turn the corner into the second half
of the first year, I thank you for your amazing grace that is and is to come.
Amen.

Write your own prayer of reflection.

_____

_____

_____

_____

_____

_____

_____

_____

Journal

_____

_____

_____

_____

_____

_____

_____

_____

_____

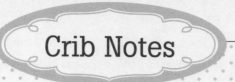

Crib Notes

Months Four to Six

Mommy's Heart—Find pure joy in this season. Baby's personality is developing, and so is his familiarity with you, mom. Let his smiles and coos bring you joy that carries you through each day (Ps. 28:7).

Baby's Development—Continue daily tummy time as baby gets ready to roll. Baby's grasp is developing, so he may reach out for toys. He will begin to coo and squeal at this stage and may begin to sit up with support.

Feeding—Breastfeeding: 15–30 minutes every 3–4 hours. Bottle-feeding: 6–7 ounces every 4 hours. Solid foods can be started during this period, preferably toward the end of this stage.

Sleeping—9–12 hours at night with two to four 30-minute to 2-hour naps throughout the day.

Play—Place a toy just out of baby's reach and watch him move to grasp it. Sing songs to your baby daily. He'll soon light up when he hears his favorite tune. Begin to teach baby peekaboo, which will likely become a favorite soon.

Personality Plus

Baby Stats

By seven months, babies range from 15 to 22 pounds (6.8–10.2 kg) in weight and approximately 25½ to 28½ inches (65–73 cm) in length.

Development Checker at Seven Months

Typical Skills

- ❑ Reaches for and drags toys toward himself
- ❑ Babbles often
- ❑ Imitates sounds
- ❑ Turns toward sounds and voices
- ❑ Recognizes familiar faces
- ❑ Sits with little to no support
- ❑ Stands and bounces when held up
- ❑ Plays with hands by bringing them together
- ❑ Pushes up on hands when on stomach
- ❑ Sees small objects such as crumbs on the floor
- ❑ Likes looking at himself in the mirror

Concerning Signs

- ❑ Seems overly stiff or overly floppy
- ❑ Does not reach for objects
- ❑ Cannot bear weight on legs

Language

Your baby's language skills are still developing, so talking and singing to your baby is very important at this stage. Some babies may advance from making oo's and ah's to using repetitive consonants ("ba ba ba" or "da da da") around this time. There are no meaningful words expected at this age. Baby is just practicing the sounds he hears. It may not seem like it, but your baby is listening to your every word, so continue to read to him often. Hearing you read greatly helps develop his language skills. At first, he will probably try to eat every book you present to him. Babies often want to chew on books more than look at the pages. This is expected, and there is no need to discourage him. It is still helpful for him to learn to hold the book and enjoy this special bonding time with you. Look for board books and plastic books that can withstand lots of drool and little teeth marks.

If your baby is not babbling or starting to imitate sounds by seven months, it may indicate that he has a speech delay or hearing loss. In some babies, this can be an effect of frequent ear infections. Babies who constantly have fluid in their inner ears basically have the same poor hearing ability as someone who is under water. If your baby has had frequent ear infections, you should be even more diligent in watching for proper speech development. He may have passed his hearing screen at the hospital, yet still have partial hearing loss. Babies with partial hearing loss will still startle to loud sounds, turn their heads to look at sounds, and even respond to your voice. However, they might not be able to imitate speech. This is the age to really talk to your child, even while doing mundane household chores. Watch closely and let his pediatrician know if you have any concerns about his speech development.

Movement

Your baby will start sitting up by six to seven months. At first, he will likely need support, either from you or by being propped up with pillows or furniture. He may be able to "tripod"—sit by extending his arms out to the floor in front of him. He will likely still "tip over" very easily at this age, so be careful where you leave him sitting, that no hard objects or sharp corners are nearby.

Social Interaction

Separation Anxiety. This often dreaded issue is a normal developmental milestone for most babies. Separation anxiety occurs when baby experiences stress due to his mother or other trusted caregiver leaving his presence. Baby does not yet understand time so he cannot grasp the fact that his loved one will return. Separation anxiety typically starts when baby is between six and nine months of age, though it can begin sooner or later. It typically lasts until baby is eighteen months, but may last into early elementary school in some children. Refer to Month Eight for more information on separation anxiety.

Play Time. Babies are able to recognize faces now. Perhaps one of his favorite faces will be his own. You may notice that your baby enjoys looking into mirrors with you and making faces. Floor toys that have built-in mirrors can be a great source of entertainment.

At around this age, babies also begin to learn a concept called "object permanence." Early in infancy, if you hid one of baby's toys under a blanket, he thought it was gone. When you left the room, he thought you were gone instead of just in the hallway. Now, he will realize that the object didn't really go anywhere. This newfound knowledge makes games such as peekaboo much more fun. He will light up when you walk back in the room or peek back out from behind a blanket.

The "uh-oh game" is also fun for baby at around seven months. Because your baby is beginning to understand cause and effect, you'll find that one of his favorite things to do is drop a toy and watch you pick it up. His sense of humor will shine through as he giggles at how funny it is to make you bend over!

Babies at seven months can begin to imitate what they see. By imitating faces and sounds, your baby will learn how to interact and communicate with you. Stick out your tongue and make silly noises to your baby. Before long, you'll find that he can do them back to you.

Make sure that all of baby's toys are unbreakable and lightweight. They should also be large enough that they are not a choking hazard. Babies put everything in their mouths now. A good rule of thumb is that objects should not be able to fit through a toilet paper roll—anything smaller is a choking risk.

Don't worry about buying expensive toys that claim to make your baby smarter. Remember, Albert Einstein didn't grow up with an iPad full of apps. A simple wooden spoon and a plastic bowl can entertain a baby for thirty minutes or more.

Baby Care

Feeding

You may be wondering how the introduction of solid foods will affect your breast or bottle-feeding routine. For some babies, solid foods will not change their milk intake at all. After all, the overwhelming majority of a baby's nutrition is still from breast milk or formula at this stage, so you do not need to restrict your child's milk intake. Other babies do seem to start to substitute solids for milk. For example, if baby eats a serving of Stage 1 baby food for lunch (typically in 2–2½ ounce servings), you may find that he takes only 4 ounces instead of his normal 6-ounce bottle of formula. As he moves to Stage 2 foods, he will likely substitute solids for milk even more. Commercially-prepared Stage 2 foods are thicker and typically come in 4-ounce servings.

Breastfed babies are usually on a good schedule by now, with daytime feedings about every three hours and no nighttime feedings. If you are breastfeeding and your baby is still waking multiple times during the night, consider that this may be from habit and not from true hunger. Especially if he latches on for only two or three minutes and then falls asleep, he probably was not truly hungry and just needed soothing. It is appropriate and often helpful to hold him off and soothe him in other ways at this point.

For formula-fed babies, you can expect that baby is probably taking anywhere from 6 to 8 ounces per bottle. Typically, he will want a morning bottle as soon as he wakes up. The rest of the day may vary.

Possible Feeding Times for a Seven-Month-Old

7 A.M. – breastfeeding or bottle-feeding
8 A.M. – cereal with fruit
11 A.M. – milk
1 P.M. – serving of vegetables or fruit

3 to 4 P.M. – milk
6 P.M. – serving of fruit and vegetable
8 P.M. – bedtime milk

Food Allergies

You may hear that you should avoid foods such as eggs and fish in the first year to prevent allergies. There is no evidence that avoiding these nutrient-rich foods until after baby's birthday will prevent an allergy later in life. The primary foods to avoid are anything hard that could be a choking hazard and raw honey prior to twelve months, due to the risk of infant botulism. Peanut butter should be avoided due to the thick, sticky texture and potential as a choking hazard. If you or another family member have life-threatening anaphylactic food allergies, your doctor may advise you a little differently regarding food avoidance in your baby. Ask your allergist if you have a family history of food allergies and if she would recommend waiting longer for your baby to start certain potential trigger foods. Refer to Month Eight for more information on food allergies.

Sleep and Schedules

Babies are usually down to two naps at this point: one midmorning and one in the afternoon. The introduction of solid foods and more defined meal times will often determine your baby's schedule at this age. Remember that babies cannot tell time, so your child may not adhere to a strict schedule every day. The routine is more important than the exact time each activity happens.

Possible Schedule of a Seven-Month-Old

7 A.M. – wake/milk feeding
8 A.M. – breakfast
9 A.M. – nap
11 A.M. – wake/milk feeding
1 P.M. – lunch

2 P.M. – nap
3 to 4 P.M. – wake/milk feeding
6 P.M. – dinner
8 P.M. – bedtime

Keep in mind this is a sample and approximate schedule to give you an idea of what your baby may be doing at this point. Do not let yourself feel wrong if your baby is doing something different. Every baby is unique. If this schedule looks appealing to you, gently guide your baby to this routine, but do not allow yourself to feel defeated if he doesn't cooperate or takes his time getting used to it.

Teething

Your baby may have cut his first tooth by now. Most babies will get a new tooth about once a month for the next few months, and by twelve months of age, they usually have four to six teeth. You should gently clean baby's teeth by brushing them with a soft toothbrush and water. Ask your doctor whether you need to give him extra fluoride. If your tap water is from a well, or the area where you live has water that is not fluoridated, your doctor may prescribe an appropriate fluoride supplement until your child is ready for regular toothpaste. To avoid cavities, you should clean your baby's teeth daily. In addition, don't let him drink juices all day or go to bed with a bottle of milk, as the sugars from these drinks can stick to the teeth and lead to cavities.

Although it is "officially" recommended (by the AAP and the ADA) that your baby start seeing a dentist as soon as he has teeth, most parents find it unrealistic to take a six-month-old to the dentist. In fact, some family dentists won't start seeing a child until he is at least two or three years old. If you have a strong family history of tooth decay and dental issues, I suggest adhering to the earlier recommendation. Your child should probably see a pediatric dentist by age one so that his teeth can be watched closely. Let your child's doctor know if you see any discoloration to his teeth so she can help you decide if you need to take your child to the dentist.

Baby Safety

CPR. As we mentioned earlier in the book, infant CPR is an important skill for new parents, grandparents, and caregivers to have in case of an emergency. Many areas offer infant CPR classes through a local hospital or the Red Cross. If you have not been trained yet, find a local class to equip yourself as soon as possible so you will be prepared if your baby needs CPR or choking relief. You can also learn these life-saving techniques using a program called Infant CPR Anytime. This kit is available through the American Heart Association and consists of a training DVD and practice mannequin. Using these tools will help you understand basic infant CPR and choking relief in about twenty minutes. The kit can be ordered and delivered to your home; it can be reviewed to refresh your skills as often as needed. Visit the American Heart Association website for more information.

Expectations for Your Doctor Visits

There is no scheduled well check for seven-month-olds. Your child may have a checkup this month if he has been slightly off-schedule on visits. Use this opportunity to catch up on missed vaccines and to ask questions about any developmental concerns that you may have.

By now you should know your pediatrician pretty well. Your baby has been through the difficult first weeks home from the hospital and has had at least three well checks and sets of vaccines. Hopefully you feel comfortable calling your child's doctor and discussing important questions. Your relationship with your child's pediatrician is extremely important because the care of your child is a partnership between you, the parent, and his doctor, the medical expert. You should always work together in caring for your baby with trust and respect. If you find you are having trust issues with your child's doctor then discuss your concerns immediately.

Not only are you learning to read your baby's cues, but his doctor has also seen him enough to know when something doesn't seem quite right. The time span between the six-month and the nine-month checkup is huge in terms of development. If you have any concerns at all that your baby is not meeting milestones, please don't wait until his nine-month appointment. Early intervention has been proven to produce better outcomes in the cases of speech and motor delays.

Common Questions You May Have This Month

My baby was put on reflux medication several months ago. How do I know if he has grown out of it and can stop the medication?

This is a very common question and one that can be addressed in several ways. If your baby seems to have no further symptoms of reflux at all, you can discuss with your doctor simply stopping the medicine "cold turkey." Often, by now, baby has outgrown his reflux. Another way is to simply leave the dose constant and not weight-adjust it anymore. As your baby continues to grow and gain weight, he may get to a point where he is only taking a small fraction of the medicine that is recommended for his weight. If the symptoms do not recur despite being on such a low dose, it is probably fine to stop it altogether. Speak with his doctor and find out her recommendations. Some babies have symptoms that linger, and they may need to be on medication longer. Remind your pediatrician if your baby is still symptomatic so she can recalculate the appropriate dose for his size.

I feel like I've gotten into a good groove with my baby, but I still feel really down most of the time. Could I be experiencing postpartum depression?

It's normal to still feel tired, frustrated, and anxious at times, but if at seven months you are still feeling down most of the time, then you are likely experiencing postpartum depression. Practical symptoms of postpartum depression include not enjoying your hobbies; not finding time for yourself; having crying spells, loss of libido, or loss of energy; and thinking of running away or escaping. Multiple therapies are available, so please talk to your OB if these symptoms are similar to what you are experiencing. This should be a beautiful and precious time in your life, not one spent in the depths of sadness and depression. Refer back to our extensive discussion of PPD in Month Three.

Mommy Care

If you find yourself still carrying around some of your baby weight or if you find it challenging to focus on healthy habits, do not get too discouraged. You focused on the baby growing inside of you for nine months. It may take at least nine months to get back to healthy habits and a healthy weight. As I mentioned in Month Two, focus on a diet full of fruits, vegetables, and lean proteins while avoiding fried and processed foods. Refer to the sample postpartum menu in the Appendix of this book.

If you find you need to lose more than twenty pounds, you may require a formal diet program. One of the best options for new moms is Weight Watchers. They have a modification in their plan for breastfeeding moms and an easy-to-use smartphone app. There are many free apps available for tracking calories, carbs, and exercise. Determine your own strategy and find the tools that will keep you on track.

If you haven't had the wherewithal to focus on your own health before this point, this might be an ideal time to step it up a notch. Realize also that some women will continue to carry extra fat stores until they are finished breastfeeding. This is your body's way of making sure you have enough reserved energy to care for you and your baby.

Sample Menu Plan

Day 1	Day 2	Day 3
Breakfast: Whole grain cereal w/ skim milk Berries Scrambled egg	**Breakfast:** Sandwich with Canadian bacon, egg, cheese and whole wheat toast Milk	**Breakfast:** Whole wheat toast w/ Peanut butter Milk
Snack: Apple with peanut butter	**Snack:** Banana	**Snack:** Pita chips w/ hummus
Lunch: Salad (spinach or dark greens) Grilled chicken Mandarin oranges Yogurt with granola	**Lunch:** Vegetable beef soup Brown rice 2 chocolate chip cookies	**Lunch:** Small hamburger Orange or side salad Yogurt
Snack: Raw almonds Milk	**Snack:** 2 servings of string cheese	**Snack:** Low sugar granola bar
Dinner: Whole wheat pasta Tomato sauce Broccoli	**Dinner:** Salmon Baked sweet potato Side salad Wheat bread	**Dinner:** Chicken and broccoli stir fry Brown rice Ice cream

The following tips may give you some ideas and motivation for your weight loss journey.

Don't buy junk. When you are up at 3 A.M. with a crying baby, and there are M&M's on the counter, you are going to grab a handful.

Don't let small failures turn into big failures. If you eat french fries for lunch, don't just write the whole day off and pig out for dinner. Healthy eating is about moderation.

Realize that soon this baby will be watching everything you put in your mouth. You need to be a good example.

Exercise

I have personally learned to enjoy exercise over the years. Notice I said *learned*. At first, getting up at 5 A.M. to run felt like a chore. I still have to fight the urge to hit snooze some mornings, but it helps to remember how much better I feel when I'm done. I can tell a huge difference in my energy and mood levels on days I exercise. Finding time to exercise after baby is a challenge. The key is to do something you enjoy to get moving. If you don't have time to do an hour spin class at the gym, at least walk with baby in a stroller around the block or do a twenty-minute exercise DVD. Aerobic exercise can reduce the symptoms of postpartum depression in addition to helping your energy, health, and weight loss.

Being overly aggressive with exercise early on can lead to injury. It's important to slowly increase your activity and avoid overdoing it. When breastfeeding and exercising, remember to increase your water intake to compensate and to also take your calcium faithfully.

Toning with weights or Pilates exercises can strengthen your core muscles that have been weakened by pregnancy and delivery. Following are some tips and motivation to encourage you on your exercise journey.

Mix socializing and exercise. Join a stroller club or running group. This holds you accountable, and exercising with friends—especially other moms—makes the time go faster. It can also be a great way to keep up with friends who aren't moms.

Hire a personal trainer. This is the highest level of accountability. You have it on the schedule, and you have to go. A lot of fitness centers offer group training if one-on-one is too expensive.

Sleep. On nights where you are up all night with the baby, choose sleep over exercise. Then hold yourself accountable not to skip after the night you actually do get some rest.

More on Sleep

It's genuinely challenging to be healthy when you aren't getting enough sleep. This I can speak to personally. When I'm up all night delivering babies, the next day all I want to do is drink coffee and eat donuts. But I don't (eat donuts, that is—coffee is a necessity in the obstetrics business!). You have to give yourself time to recuperate on days when you are sleep-deprived. If you have to choose between exercise and sleep, choose sleep. Rest your body. Sleep when the baby sleeps. Rest your body, but avoid falling into the simple-carb trap. Our bodies crave sugary carbohydrates when we are tired. They make you feel good only briefly, but the energy they provide is fleeting, and soon you will be crashing worse than before.

Wellness

At least once a month, as I am interviewing a new patient, I will ask how long it's been since she had a Pap, and she will say with a laugh, "I haven't been to a doctor since my last baby was born!" Sadly, some of their "babies" are thirty years old. As moms, our own health often gets put on the back burner.

An annual exam, whether with your OB-GYN or primary care doctor, is still the recommendation. The Pap smear guidelines have changed several times over the last few years, but regardless of your recommended Pap interval, you still need an annual exam. Mammograms are recommended at age forty or earlier if you have a strong family history of breast cancer.

Mammograms are safe while breastfeeding; however, due to dense tissue, they are not as accurate. A flu shot and pertussis vaccine (for whooping cough) is recommend for new moms as well as all family members in contact with a young baby.

A Real-Life Story

Being A Full Time Working Mom

Jess— mom to Brody and Kellen

When I was pregnant with my oldest son, I fully intended to go back to work. I had watched many friends gracefully exit once their precious bundles arrived. I had no reason though to think I would be following in their footsteps. In my mind, it was just another one of life's transitions.

Fast forward through four attempts at an epidural, a full day's worth of labor, and thirty minutes of pushing, and out came the most beautiful red-headed baby I'd ever seen. Immediately, it was like someone flipped a switch in my heart. I couldn't even remember my well-thought-out plan as I was thrust into my new role and operating on little or no sleep. I had no idea how to handle the two roles I'd been given. I remember thinking that I was certain God had given me both this precious life to nurture as well as a job I truly loved. I would trust him to teach me to juggle them both.

I spent the greater part of our son's first year doubting my decision to go back to work, wondering if I'd miss out on so much that I'd regret later. I did few things well because I was trying so hard to be everything I thought I should be to everyone.

Now we've been blessed with two amazing boys and I'm still working. The truth is that I don't feel I have missed out on anything. My husband and I have purposely made every decision around what we believe works for our family. We are determined to be a team, and without his help, none of this would work. Our daycare is right next to my work. I can walk there and I have spent many of my lunch breaks with my boys. I've even thrown birthday parties in their classrooms. I managed to breastfeed both boys exclusively for the first year of their lives. We haven't sacrificed anything that mattered because we put clear boundaries around what we wanted for our family and what was not negotiable. God has blessed us abundantly by providing us with peace around our decisions.

In my motherhood journey, I've learned that it's not about juggling. It's not my job to keep the balls from dropping, but I have found a sense of humor if they do. And I can't hold them tightly in my hands either; I have to live open handed and be present in each and every moment I have with my children. I am intentional in the boundaries I set so that I don't miss out on the things that matter. These would be my goals even if I stayed home. I'm okay to not change every diaper, but I want to be there when they have questions about girls or have soccer games. We might not have homemade meals every night, but we'll eat together as much as we can.

Being a working mother, for now, makes me better for them because it forces me to make every moment count. I don't know that I'll always be a working mom. I've asked God to help me parent through the seasons and be open to what he calls me to do. Who knows, someday I might stay home and be a room mom. I am going to leave my hands and my heart wide open and enjoy the journey.

Truth for the Journey

"Devote yourselves to prayer, being watchful and thankful." Colossians 4:2

You are rounding the corner of baby's first year, mama. Now that you have settled in and are feeling less stressed, I want to encourage you to focus in on your baby's heart and mind. You've gotten into a groove on feeding, diapering, and (hopefully) sleep. As your baby's personality begins to bloom, it's time to set your attention on the little person he is becoming.

One of the most important aspects of being a mom is learning your baby. For the past six months, you've learned his cues, what each cry means, and what routine works best for him. These discoveries have helped you lead and guide your little one throughout his days. As he begins to develop his personality, it's time to take your learning to the next level.

By the time my little man was seven months old, I could tell that he was curious and inquisitive. When he discovered something new, he wanted to know more. He paid attention to every little detail of his toys and his surroundings. I knew then that he was going to be on the move. Sure enough, six months later he is mobile and into just about everything. Nothing gets by this kid. (He's a lot like his mommy!) Understanding his personality early on has helped me prepare to nurture this trait by setting boundaries that will keep him safe while allowing him to explore.

Months one through six are largely spent meeting your baby's physical needs. Food, clothing, diapering, sleep—all of these essentials are a given. Besides the difference in preferences we hold as moms (or the occasional dietary exception), each of our babies needs the same things. Yet when we consider the emotional needs of children, they couldn't be more different—even at seven months of age.

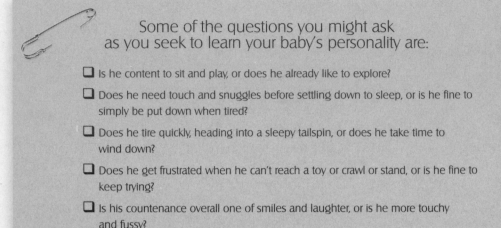

Some of the questions you might ask
as you seek to learn your baby's personality are:

❑ Is he content to sit and play, or does he already like to explore?

❑ Does he need touch and snuggles before settling down to sleep, or is he fine to simply be put down when tired?

❑ Does he tire quickly, heading into a sleepy tailspin, or does he take time to wind down?

❑ Does he get frustrated when he can't reach a toy or crawl or stand, or is he fine to keep trying?

❑ Is his countenance overall one of smiles and laughter, or is he more touchy and fussy?

To some extent, babies carry all of these traits. Most of them get frustrated when they can't do something, and most like to explore their surroundings. But if you truly study your little one, you'll find he favors certain behaviors; knowing this will empower you to love and lead him well.

If I could encourage you to do one thing right now, mom, it's to engage in deep prayer over the completion of year one and prepare yourself for the toddler years. While I don't want you to rush through these precious months as you look ahead to the next season, it's never too early to pray for what is coming. As you learn your baby's unique personality, you can pray more specifically for his life. As you practice committed prayer for your child, you will grow a deeper mother's love as God reveals his heart for your baby. Nothing will better prepare you for the next season of motherhood, both spiritually and emotionally.

We'll talk more about preparing yourself to parent a toddler in Month Ten, but right now I just encourage you to pray. I know you have been praying over your little one from the moment you discovered he was growing in your womb. As your pregnancy progressed, and then as you welcomed him into your arms, your prayers grew. And your prayers will continue to grow as your child grows, becoming more and more purposeful and intense.

Managing Baby's Gear

Dealing with countless baby items can be overwhelming. After four years and two children, I still have bins of clothes and gear in various corners of my home. Some are awaiting an upcoming consignment sale, while others are precious memorabilia I cannot seem to part with. With baby outgrowing clothes, toys, and gear so quickly in the first year, it's best to have a plan for dealing with all of his stuff. In addition, if you are planning to have another child in the near future, you will need a system of organization as you keep much of baby's clothing, toys, and gear around for his sibling.

Clothes. You have moved through clothes quickly in the past six months and will continue to do so. If baby's closet permits the space, label three bins: "next season," "give away," and "keep." With baby's current clothes hanging or folded in drawers, you can use these bins to organize and sort what he is not able to wear any longer or those clothing items you are keeping for the next season or size. Keep track of your local consignment sale dates so you have time to prepare if you plan to sell your items.

Toys. You may begin with the intention not to have too many toys for your baby, but between eager grandparents, aunts, and your best friend who is trying to get rid of old toys, you may very well be drowning in a sea of plastic. Utilize small bins or baskets, and place toys in various rooms throughout your house. You can also place a small bin of toys in your car. One trick I know many moms use is to store some toys for a while and rotate through them every few weeks or months. If you find there are simply too many toys for baby to play with, don't feel like you have to keep them all. Similar to your clothing system, you can sort your toys into various bins as well. Label these bins "next month," "give away," and "keep."

Gear. Your baby gear will take up the most space in your home. A stroller, play yard, and swing are major appliances that can easily get in the way. Many items will be obsolete within the first nine months of baby's life. Once you are through with his swing and ExerSaucer, for instance, find a space in your garage or attic to store the items if you plan to have another child. If you do not have the space, consider loaning the items to a friend or family member who is having a baby. Once they cycle through the gear, you may be ready to have it back for another child. When you are ready to part with these items, look for a local consignment sale or shop where you can sell it. Well-kept baby gear will usually fetch a good price at these sales. Craigslist is also a great place to unload your gear.

Using Facebook to Buy and Sell Clothing, Toys, and Gear

Many areas have private Facebook groups that you can join to buy and sell items within your community. This is a great way to quickly unload your items and pick up things you might need for a fraction of the cost. Ask around in your city to see if a local neighborhood or organization has this type of Facebook group. Typically, you will need to be invited, as participants want members to be local and trustworthy.

Taking Care of Yourself

If you find that you are discouraged and frustrated with yourself for not being back in shape at this point, I get it. I really do. Many moms find it harder than they thought it would be to lose their baby weight. As Dr. Rupe encouraged, focus on a strategy that includes a well-balanced diet and moderate exercise.

As you fall into a good routine with baby, it will be much easier to plan and strategize for taking care of yourself. Spend some time reflecting on what you've been able to do thus far. If you've worked hard but hit a plateau, it may be time to revise your plan. If you've not yet started to work diligently on getting back into shape, now is the time. Focusing on yourself, mama, is incredibly hard no matter where you are on your wellness journey. Between feedings, diapers, playtime, cooking, cleaning . . . it's somewhat laughable to think about adding in strategic meal planning and exercise (especially if you have more than one child in your home). But there is great grace, my friend. Grace that covers every one of those tasks and leaves room for more. It will require diligence. It will require strategy and planning. It will require the will to break through exhaustion and apathy. But it's possible.

Trust the Lord to be near as you travel the road to wellness. He cares deeply about your well-being. The same God who so intricately created you desires for your body to be at its optimum potential, which will bring the most glory to him. This very well may be a place of battle for you. It continues to be for me. Let's focus on the truth of who God made us as we find the will to discover our greatest potential.

Now that you've had a baby, though, you may find your "greatest potential" is different than it was before your pregnancy. This can be very discouraging. Your body has gone through a huge change with having a baby, and this change can have an equally large effect on your body image. If you find yourself becoming resentful of what having a baby has done to your body, I encourage you to lay those thoughts before God and ask him to show you the beautiful truth about who you are—stretch marks and all. The psalmist wrote, "For you created my inmost being; you knit me together in my mother's womb. I praise you because I am fearfully and wonderfully made; your works are wonderful, I know that full well. My frame was not hidden from you when I was made in the secret place. When I was woven together in the depths of the earth, your eyes saw my unformed body. All the days ordained for me were written in your book before one of them came to be. . . . Search me, O God, and know my heart; test me and know my anxious thoughts. See if there is any offensive way in me, and lead me in the way everlasting" (Ps. 139:13–16, 23–24). Meditate on these verses as you think about your image of yourself and as you purpose to celebrate your baby—the fruit of your labor. You were both fearfully and wonderfully made. Do not lose your own worth as you focus on your baby. You are as precious to the Father as your little one is. You both matter so very much. Let this truth drive your love for your child *and* your desire to be the best mom you can be, both emotionally and physically.

Even as you try to focus more on yourself now, mom, remember to keep a heart of gratitude. Our key verse for this month touches on what I've shared about being watchful and devoting ourselves to prayer, but the most powerful message in this verse is at its end. "Devote yourselves to prayer, being watchful and *thankful*." I'm sure your gratitude also grows with each passing day as you watch your baby develop. A heart of thanks is the root of every single thing you need as a mom. So in the midst of your crazy days, and especially as you begin to encounter a new level of exhaustion from chasing after a mobile baby, thank the God of heaven for the living and active blessing of this child. What a gift you have been given.

Prayer Concerns

Baby's developing nature

A heart of gratitude

Eyes to see my baby's personality

Grace for taking care of myself

A Prayer for This Month

Dear Lord,

How exciting it is to see my baby's personality bloom. Give me eyes to see the little person you are creating. Help me to see deep into my child's heart. I desire to cultivate a heart of gratitude, Father, even in the midst of busy days, because you are awesome and faithful and worthy of my praise. Thank you for the privilege of being mom to this precious life. Amen.

Write your own prayer of reflection.

_____

_____

_____

_____

Journal

_____

_____

_____

_____

_____

Sweet Mobility

Baby Stats

By eight months, babies range from 15½ to 23 pounds (7–10.5 kg) in weight and approximately 26 to 29½ inches (66–75 cm) in length.

Development Checker at Eight Months

Typical Skills

- ❑ Sits well without support
- ❑ Pushes up on hands and knees, rocking
- ❑ Begins to scoot or crawl
- ❑ Begins to pick up small pieces of food and self-feed

Concerning Signs

- ❑ Overly "serious," doesn't seem to like eye contact and games

Language

By now, you can expect your baby to be babbling often and imitating sounds. He may be able to make one or two consonant sounds, such as "ba ba" or "da da." These sounds are usually not associated with a specific person or object at this age. If your baby is not yet attempting to make consonant sounds, tell his pediatrician. It could be a sign of partial hearing loss. Babies with partial hearing loss will still respond to sounds and make babbling noises, but they may not be able to demonstrate fuller language development. Most babies will be nine to twelve months old before they utter the much-anticipated "Dada" and "Mama." Continue to read aloud and talk to your baby to help develop his language skills during this very crucial time.

Movement

Your baby may be able to transfer objects from one hand to the other by this age. Give your baby age-appropriate toys and objects that he can practice with. Remember, these objects are likely going to end up in his mouth, too, so be sure to give clean, safe toys and nothing that could be a choking hazard.

Baby should be sitting alone well for extended periods without needing any support or propping up. Nearly all babies have this skill by eight months, though there may be a small percentage of children who take until nine months to master sitting without support, particularly if they were born prematurely. If your baby is making no effort to sit alone by now, you should talk with his pediatrician.

Even after your baby is sitting well, remember he should still be kept in a safe area where he will not get hurt if he falls over. Babies will lunge quickly toward something they want and make no attempts to "catch" themselves at this age. Watch out for sharp corners on the fireplace, entertainment centers, coffee tables, and other furniture. Never leave baby sitting alone on a couch or a bed. He will almost always find his way off of a high surface. Your baby will also start to scoot and maybe even crawl by eight months. Several periods of tummy time every day are still vital to these motor skill developments.

Spotting a shiny trinket across the room or seeing an open cupboard in the kitchen is all the motivation baby will need to learn to crawl. At first, he will learn to push up on his hands. Next, he'll figure out how to pull those knees up under himself and sit on all fours. Most babies will rock back and forth for at least several weeks before figuring out how to go anywhere. A baby's arm strength and coordination often develop more quickly than that of his legs. You may find that baby can push backward with his arms before he learns to put one in front of the other to move forward. Sit on the floor with him and encourage him with praise and his favorite toys. Baby will be on the move soon, so remember to baby proof all living areas to prevent injury.

Your baby's vision is developing even more clearly as well, which is why he may find even the tiniest objects on the floor and in carpeting. For example, if you lost the back of an earring a few months ago—leave it to a baby to find it. Try to make sure no small objects are left lying about and vacuum often to keep baby's play area clean.

A frequent concern for parents is the appearance of baby's feet and legs. Babies tend to have flat feet at birth, and this often persists past the toddler stage. One reason babies appear to have flat feet is that they tend to have a fat pad on the inner side of the bottoms of their feet, which covers and hides the natural arch of the foot. Additionally, babies' bones and joints are very flexible still, and when they stand up, the pressure causes their feet to flatten. This is a normal finding in babies and not a reason for concern. Your baby does not need special shoes or shoe inserts to correct his chubby, flat feet.

Sometimes babies' feet appear to be turned in. If the front part of your baby's foot curves in or makes him appear pigeon-toed, there is likely no need for alarm. This condition is called metatarsus adductus. It is often related to the position of your baby in the womb. In a majority of cases, metatarsus adductus will self-correct by six to eight months of age and will not require any intervention. If it persists, or in very severe cases where the baby has a true congenital clubfoot, your doctor may refer your child to a pediatric orthopedist who can treat him appropriately. Your child's pediatrician will examine his feet and legs at every checkup and let you know if she thinks he has any issues out of the ordinary.

After baby starts standing and walking, his feet may appear to be turning out. This is a common finding and is due to increased flexibility of his ligaments. As his ligaments and muscles strengthen, his feet will gradually appear to turn back in. This usually occurs by age two or three at the latest.

Babies also often appear bow-legged at this age. Your baby may like to stand up on his feet while holding your hands—this is when most parents will notice some mild curvature of baby's legs. In most cases, this is a normal finding at this age. As baby grows and his bones elongate and muscles develop, his legs will straighten up nicely. This mild bowing of the legs will not affect his walking. If your baby's legs look especially bowed, or if he seems excessively clumsy when trying to stand with support, then you should let your pediatrician know. His doctor will want to check his hips, knees, and ankles for any signs of concern.

Social Interaction

Separation/Stranger Anxiety. In the past few months, you've probably noticed baby becoming more attached to you. This is due to the normal, developmental stages of stranger anxiety and separation anxiety. Stranger anxiety usually comes first. As mentioned in Month Six, babies are now able to differentiate between familiar and unfamiliar people and places. Before now, your baby may have smiled and cooed back at every smiling face in the grocery store. He may have allowed just about anyone to pick him up and pass him around. This comfort level often drastically decreases at this age. Even relatives and frequent babysitters will suddenly notice that baby no longer goes to them as easily, particularly if he is approached too suddenly. This can be particularly upsetting to grandparents. Try to give reassurance that it is a normal stage of development. It is not because baby is "spoiled" or held too much by his mother.

Separation anxiety usually comes next. For months, you may have been able to easily hand off baby to a caregiver prior to going out of the house. Now, you may experience baby clinging to you or crying when you leave. Babies have no sense of time at this age, so when he sees you leave, he does not know when you will be coming back. Seeing his mother leave a room can thus be a great source of distress for him. Hold your child close and talk to him in a soft, soothing voice before you leave him. Rushing off quickly "before he notices" can make separation anxiety worse. When it is time to go, reassure him that you will be back soon, and hand him off to whomever will be taking care of him while you are away. Babies will typically calm more quickly if they are with a known caregiver who can cuddle and reassure them. Try to distract him with an activity that he enjoys.

Baby Care

Feeding

Food allergies are on the rise. It seems that everyone now knows a family that has a child with food allergies. Whether it is peanuts, eggs, or milk, it is definitely a source of stress and difficulty for those families affected.

A common first sign of a food allergy is a simple rash. My own child was diagnosed with an allergy to eggs just after his first birthday. On two separate occasions, we gave him scrambled eggs to eat. In both instances, he developed a faint, blotchy, pink rash right around his mouth. It was so subtle I almost didn't see it. We stopped feeding him the egg, and within twenty to thirty minutes, the rash was gone. I discussed the rash with two of my partners at work, and we all agreed that he should probably be tested. Sure enough, his skin allergy test came up positive.

Some common reactions that can occur with a food allergy:

- Rashes—This can be anything from blotchy skin to full-blown hives with swelling.
- Breathing problems—This is the more classic and serious scenario, where a child has shortness of breath and wheezing shortly after ingesting a particular food.
- Stomach issues—Nausea and vomiting are possible with a food allergy and can be mistaken for a viral illness.

("Food Allergy: Tips to Remember," www.aaaai.org; "Food Allergies in Children," healthychildren.org; "Outgrowing," FAAN, www.foodallergy.org.)

As your child continues to try new foods, you should watch for any signs of food allergy like those listed above. If he is having a serious reaction, you should call 911 immediately. Even for a mild reaction, your child's doctor should be notified right away, and the suspicious food should be avoided altogether until allergy testing can be performed.

While many food allergies do not tend to run in families, some (like peanuts) can be more common if there are siblings who are highly allergic. If serious anaphylactic food allergies run in your family, your child's pediatrician should be notified. You will want to consider having your child seen for a consult with an allergist prior to his first birthday.

The good news is that many food allergies are not lifelong. According to the AAP and the American Academy of Allergy, Asthma and Immunology, over half of children with egg, milk, or soy allergies will eventually outgrow them, perhaps as early as kindergarten. Some children may not outgrow their allergies until their teenage years, and others will have them for life. Peanut and shellfish allergies are less likely to be outgrown.

Sleep and Schedules

If your baby still isn't sleeping through the night, you may feel very discouraged. The first key is to figure out why he is waking up during the night and what is keeping him awake. Is he used to falling asleep in the living room or in bed with you? If he wakes up and finds himself in his own crib, he may not be able to get himself back to sleep, since that is not his routine. Is he used to being rocked to sleep? He may not yet have developed the self-soothing skills to put himself back to sleep without being rocked. Are you feeding him every time he wakes up? Is he only taking 1 or 2 ounces and then falling back asleep? If so, his waking is most likely from habit and he is not truly hungry—he just associates feeding with sleep. If you are co-sleeping, this can be an age when baby just wants to wake up and play. He sees you lying there and thinks, "Hey! Mommy is fun! Let's play!" and therefore cannot relax to go back to sleep.

There may also be physical reasons your baby cannot sleep. He will likely be getting one or more teeth nonstop for the next few months. He may be in pain and experience frequent waking from teething. Pain relievers and cool teething toys can be used to ease this pain and get him back to sleep.

Sleep training is tough business for lots of families. As we've mentioned before, there are numerous method books out there. Some of our favorites are listed in the Appendix at the back of this book. If you looked at a particular method before but did not follow through, revisit it and try again. Remember, after you choose a method, stick with it. The first week or two may be hard, but you can do it. You may have to go through short-term frustration for long-term gain. *Now is the time!* The longer you wait to help baby develop a sleep routine, the harder it will be. Once he can stand up in his crib and scream "Mommy!" he will be hard to resist. And that time is coming in just a few months!

Teething

Baby probably has at least one tooth by now and may have three or four. However, don't worry if he still doesn't have any at all. (It may be a blessing for you breast-feeding mamas!) Remember, there is a wide range of when to expect baby's first tooth. Don't forget to clean baby's teeth with a soft toothbrush or cloth and plain water daily.

Girl Talk/Boy Talk

Yeast infections. Yeast infections are a common rash seen in baby girls. Typically, a yeast rash will appear as a bright red, shiny skin rash, sometimes with bright red dots scattering out at the borders (these are called "satellite lesions"). You may find that your daughter continues to have yeast infections and vulvitis (inflammation of the external genitals) even through potty-training age. Yeast likes to grow in a warm, wet, dirty environment, so what better place than a diaper?

Antifungal creams such as over-the-counter Lotrimin or Monistat can be applied like diaper cream two to three times daily to heal the skin, usually for about seven to ten days. Try to change baby's diaper frequently or even allow open-air time, if that is feasible. If using cloth diapers, try vinegar or another yeast killer, such as the good old-fashioned sunshine, during your wash routine. If the rash looks particularly bad, or if it is not responding to anti-fungal medications after a few days, she should be seen by her doctor to confirm the diagnosis.

Finding his penis. Mothers don't like to think about it, but eventually your son will find his penis. I always joke with families that boys seem to find them just as fascinating now as they do for decades to come. All joking aside, just as baby spent hours looking at his hands after he found them, boys seem to be enthralled with this newly discovered appendage. Moms are often concerned that baby is tugging and pinching at his penis. Try not to worry—if it hurts, he'll quit. You should expect baby to explore his body, and there is no reason to discourage him from doing so.

Baby Safety

Seats. As baby gets bigger, you may be tempted to skip the buckle-in strollers and high chairs, especially those with a tray or bar that seemingly keeps baby in tight. A good rule of thumb is—if there is a restraint buckle, use it! Your baby can easily slide out of a chair or stroller as he moves about. If you become inconsistent in using the buckle in his high chair, for instance, you may forget he is not restrained and remove his tray to clean up after a meal, leaving him open to a fall. It's very easy to accidentally make these careless moves as a busy parent. This is why the buckles are there.

Poison control. Now that baby is on the move, you should have the number for your local poison control hotline posted somewhere obvious and easily accessible. Hopefully, if your home is well baby proofed, your child cannot access items that would cause him harm. Rethink the storage of items such as cleaners and pesticides, keeping them far out of baby's reach. Don't underestimate the tenacity of a curious baby. Keep the number for poison control close, but keep dangerous materials far away so you never have to use it.

Expectations for Your Doctor Visits

There is no scheduled well check for eight-month-olds. You can schedule a well check this month if he has been slightly off-schedule on visits. Use this opportunity to catch up on missed vaccines and to ask questions about any developmental concerns you may have.

Baby's development should be progressing daily. His speech and motor skills in particular should be noticeably different now than they were one month ago. Baby should have made huge milestones between his six-month and nine-month checkups. If you have any concerns at all, please don't hesitate to call his doctor for an extra visit between well checks. Early intervention has been proven to produce better results when it comes to developmental delays. Your baby's doctor can examine him and refer him to the appropriate therapists, if needed. Remember, there are no stupid questions—it's much better to have some reassurance than to have a delay go on too long.

As mentioned earlier in the book, don't hesitate to let your pediatrician's office staff know if you have major concerns about something. Bringing baby in for a quick ear check versus bringing baby in for severe or chronic vomiting or lack of developmental milestones requires a different type of consultation. Make sure the office staff know what is going on so they can schedule the appropriate amount of time for your child's visit. Your concerns are important, and your baby's doctor needs to have plenty of time set aside for your child if there are serious issues to discuss.

Common Questions You May Have This Month

My baby seems to be uncomfortable in his car seat. Is it time to switch?

Many babies are getting to the twenty-pound mark by nine months, and many infant seats are only approved up to around twenty-three pounds. It may be time to upgrade to a convertible car seat. If you do not have one already, do some research and ask friends and family their recommendations. Remember that even in a larger seat, you must keep your child rear-facing. It doesn't matter if baby's legs look "squished" or uncomfortable—rear-facing is the safest way to travel with your child. It is actually recommended to keep children rear-facing until two years old.

Why can't I give my baby peanut butter?

Despite what you may think, a potential allergy is not the biggest reason you shouldn't give your child peanut butter before he is a year old. The sticky texture of peanut butter is more of a concern, as it presents a choking hazard. Babies at this stage have not yet perfected their ability to chew and swallow, which is why they require soft, smooth-textured foods. Although you should always be cautious when first giving your baby foods with an allergy potential (nuts, eggs, and so on), this isn't the reason to avoid peanut butter at this point ("Switching to Solid Foods," healthychildren.org). Both the AAP and the American Academy of Allergy, Asthma and Immunology agree that there is no current scientific evidence that avoiding peanut butter prior to your baby's first birthday will decrease the potential for allergy. In fact, there is some current evidence that early introduction of certain foods may actually *decrease* the potential for allergy later on. For most children, offering a food that "may contain peanuts" is perfectly okay prior to age one. If there is a history of anaphylactic peanut allergy in your family, you may want to exercise more caution and introduce peanut-containing foods a little later in life and under the direction of a pediatric allergist. When you do introduce peanut butter to your baby (between twelve and eighteen months), start with a small amount on the lips or tongue to check for any allergic reaction.

Truth for the Journey

*"But the fruit of the Spirit is love, joy, peace, longsuffering, gentleness,
goodness, faith, meekness, temperance: against such there is no law. . . .
If we live in the Spirit, let us also walk in the Spirit."* Galatians 5:22–23, 25 KJV

I shared early on in the book about seeking wisdom to guide you through baby's
first year (and every year of your child's life, for that matter). The Holy Spirit is the
tool we were given after Jesus ascended into heaven to guide us through our days.
But this God-given guide is not just a source of wisdom; it is the source of other
good fruit in our lives as well. A life led by the Spirit bears much fruit. This truth is
so valuable for moms.

It would be easy to get stuck in a rut of trying to survive our mundane and
exhausting days as a mom. We've touched on this throughout the book, giving you
Scriptures and thoughts for overcoming this often-expected plight of motherhood.
I feel compelled to revisit the idea of the Spirit in greater depth because this is your
most powerful weapon against fear, confusion, exhaustion, and complacency.

Galatians 5:22–23 lays out the fruit we will see in our lives when we live by
the Spirit. This popular verse that many of us recited in our early days at Sunday
school often goes overlooked in our adult lives. We all want to see the presence of
joy, peace, patience, and gentleness in our lives, yet we forget where this yummy
fruit is rooted.

Author Angela Thomas explains a life in the Spirit in her book *Choosing Joy* this
way: "There is a difference in the person who is saved and getting by as best she can
and the person who is saved, living every day of her life filled with the power of the
Holy Spirit. . . . Becoming spiritually mature requires one degree of choosing. The
one who is becoming spiritual is being filled and refilled by the power of the presence of the Holy Spirit" (152–153; Howard Publishing, 2011).

One degree of choosing. Choosing to invite the Spirit of a living God to dwell in
you and among you throughout your days. It makes all the difference in the world,

mama. And it's the only way we are going to make it. Whether you are facing tough decisions for your little one or extenuating circumstances with his health or sleep patterns—the Holy Spirit is your source of wisdom and strength, leading to the fruit of an abundant life. Even if you are gliding through this year with few challenges, you still need the Holy Spirit guiding your life to bear good fruit.

Let's take a look at some of the fruit that comes from this one degree of choosing.

Joy. A deep well of gratitude and happiness; evidence of the presence of God in our lives. "Joy is the infallible sign of the presence of God" (Pierre Teilhard de Chardin).

Peace. An inner calm that cannot be explained by outward circumstances or appearances. "Peace. It does not mean to be in a place where there is no noise, trouble or hard work. It means to be in the midst of all of those things and still be calm in your heart" (Unknown).

Patience. The ability to wait and consider and act only when you know that you know that it's time. "Patience is the companion of wisdom" (Saint Augustine).

Kindness. The quality of being warm and considerate. "A tree is known by its fruit; a man by his deeds. A good deed is never lost; he who sows courtesy reaps friendship, and he who plants kindness gathers love" (Saint Basil).

Choose today to live a life guided by the Spirit—watch the fruit of your life grow and touch not only your family but every person you encounter along the way.

Communicating with Your Pediatrician

Dr. Johnston shared her heart this month about being available to answer even the seemingly silliest questions of moms. It's true that the only stupid question is the one you don't ask. Don't ever feel silly, embarrassed, or bad about asking your doctor a question. Your pediatrician has been trained to guide you medically as you care for your child. She went through years of grueling study and training, not to mention practice, in order to be called an expert on taking care of children. It takes lots and lots of passion to endure medical training. She is driven by her desire to partner with you. As long as you are considerate of your doctor's time and schedule, you should never feel bad for asking questions. Every doctor and every pediatric practice will have different policies for well visits, consult visits, and after-hours calls, so the very first question you should ask is how and when to ask your questions. If you are operating within their parameters, then ask away. Together, you and your pediatrician are sure to find the best course of action for your child in every situation.

Make sure you find time for yourself, mama. This can be as simple as sitting at a coffee shop to read on a Saturday morning or going on a weekend retreat with your best friend. If you haven't left your baby overnight yet, now may be a good time to give it a try. Your first night away from him may make you feel guilty and anxious, but I can assure you, your baby will not remember, let alone feel abandoned by your absence. A short retreat will only do wonders for your soul and allow you to better care for him when you return. Talk with your spouse or family and schedule a time to get away soon. If you are breastfeeding and still find it hard to get away for extended periods of time, try scheduling mini-retreats. Pump and store enough milk to sneak away for two to three hours regularly. A weekly massage or mani/pedi may be just what you need to refuel. As baby's mobility increases and his personality develops, I pray you will be able to access the sweet fruit of the Spirit so that your days with him will be abundantly blessed.

Prayer Concerns

Baby's mobility
Wisdom in food choices
Fruit of the Spirit
Mommy time

A Prayer for This Month

Dear Lord,
Thank you for the fruit that is evident through a life lived in you. I pray
that my joy, peace, patience, and kindness would be complete as I choose
to remain connected to your Spirit. As my baby becomes mobile, give me

wisdom in protecting and guiding him. Lord, I ask for you to provide time for me to be alone to rest and renew my mind. Most of all, give me grace to abide in you every moment of every day. Amen.

Write your own prayer of reflection.

Journal

Amazing Growth

Baby Stats

By nine months, babies range from 16 to 23½ pounds (7.2–10.8 kg) in weight and approximately 27 to 30 inches (68–76 cm) in length.

Development Checker at Nine Months

Typical Skills
- ❑ Stands with support
- ❑ Jabbers
- ❑ Scoots or crawls
- ❑ Says repetitive consonant and vowel sounds

Concerning Signs
- ❑ Refusal to bear weight on legs
- ❑ Minimal jabbering

Language

Get ready, mom. You've put in countless hours of feeding, rocking, soothing, bathing, snuggling, and cuddling. Yet despite all your sacrifice, your baby's first word is most likely going to be "dada." Babies have an easier time saying "dada" because "D" and "B" consonants typically come first in their language development, followed by "M." But hang in there, mama. Your time will come soon. My mom always said she taught me to say dada first, so she could stay in bed, and he'd have to get up when I started calling out in the morning.

Most babies are able to say at least one consonant sound by nine months. As mentioned before, it's usually "da" or "ba" first. If you're lucky, maybe it *will* be "ma" first. (Then you can brag to all your friends!) Babies are not able to differentiate words for a particular person, though. So baby may say "dada" to every man he sees in the grocery store. This is normal and makes for some interesting shopping trips.

Even though he cannot *say* words, baby is beginning to *understand* more and more words, so take the time to speak clearly to your child and even explain things from time to time. Speak in pleasant tones and try to avoid too much baby talk. You want him to learn not only the basic sounds but also the inflection in your voice.

There is evidence that children tend to learn new information more readily when it is set to music. Try singing to baby or playing music to him every day. He will love to watch your face and gestures as you sing silly children's songs to him, and he will be the best audience you've ever had. Make sure to clap for yourself when you're all done!

Babies enjoy learning animal sounds at a very early age. Use picture books or your backyard to point out animals and make their noises for baby. Ask, "What does a cow say?" and help him learn the proper response. At this stage, you can also teach your baby his body parts. Point to your nose and his and clearly say, "Nose." Keep in mind he will probably learn to identify your nose and eyes before he can point to his own.

Movement

Clapping. One of the first "signs" that a baby can make is to clap. At first, he'll learn to bring his hands together to hold on to toys and other objects. Soon though, he'll learn that if he claps them together, they'll make noise. Even more importantly, he sees that if he claps, you beam at him in response. Then he'll realize that both he and those around him will clap if he does something special. Watch him smile from ear to ear with pride for his accomplishments.

Crawling. Ready or not, baby can finally go places now. It may not be a perfect crawl, but where there's a will, there's a way—baby will scoot, creep, or crawl somehow to get to what he wants. Don't be alarmed if your baby's crawl isn't perfect. Lots of babies never do have that textbook alternation of hands and knees, one in front of the other. However, if baby seems to avoid using one arm or leg more than the other, inform his pediatrician right away.

Social Interaction

Your baby is getting more social every day. He's also learning how to get an emotional reaction from you. When he cries, you look sorry for him and pick him up. So when he does something good, make sure to clap and smile and go crazy over his big accomplishment. As mentioned before, he will also learn to clap and feel very proud of himself. Believe it or not, baby wants to be good and to please you. Make sure you give plenty of positive feedback every day. It's hard to believe that his self-esteem is forming already, but it is. From an early age, children need to feel constant reassurance that Mommy and Daddy are right there cheering them on.

Baby can sit up well now and move around to explore new things. Let him take time to really check things out. Baby is also still learning cause and effect. Allow him to watch water go everywhere when he splashes in the bathtub. Let him knock over a stack of blocks to see them tumble everywhere. All of this will seem brand-new and exciting. You really don't need to spend lots of money on educational or interactive baby toys now. Everyday household items are all the entertainment baby needs.

Baby Care

Feeding

Baby will still need lots of help during mealtime for now. Developmentally, it will be a while before he can hold his own spoon or fork. Use soft spoons for baby foods. If you are using prepackaged baby food, he will probably eat Stage 2 foods now. Some babies may be ready for Stage 3 foods as well at this point. Stage 3 foods have small chunks of whole food and are thicker in texture. It is fine to try these foods now, but don't worry if baby doesn't like them yet. The texture may still be too much for him to handle. Wait a month or so and try again.

Your baby is beginning to develop his pincer grasp. Right now, baby can pick up small pieces of food between his thumb and side of his second finger (the "scissor grasp"). Picking up foods with the tip of the fingers will come at about twelve months. Your baby may be ready to start small finger foods such as puffs or yogurt melts. Bits of banana or soft butter crackers are good starter finger foods as well.

Parents often ask when they can start meats for their child. Store-bought Stage 2 foods are all about the same texture, whether it be fruits, vegetables, or various combinations that include meat. There isn't an exact age when meats are suddenly fine for baby. It's more about the texture of the food and whether your baby is developmentally ready for it. If you haven't already tried meat, now is a fine time to start. If he doesn't like it, trust me—he'll let you know.

Giving juice to your baby is still optional. Your baby's main source of calories should be his milk and baby foods. Juice is basically empty calories, without much nutritional value. If you do choose to give your baby juice, dilute it with water and limit it to no more than 6 ounces per day.

Sleep and Schedules

Your baby has probably been in a predictable routine for the past few months. Isn't it nice? It's funny to look back just six or seven months ago and think about how much life has changed. Most babies are taking two naps per day and sleeping ten or eleven hours at night. If your baby still wakes for feedings every night, this may just be habit. You can gradually stretch out his nighttime feedings until he no longer wakes for them. Push back overnight feedings by fifteen minutes at a time until baby adjusts to a new schedule.

All babies should be able to sleep through the night by nine months (though that doesn't mean that they will do so willingly). Babies that still eat one to two feedings at night at this point can be weaned off of this; however, it depends on how strict you, as the mom, want to be. If you can stand to stretch him out and have a few rough nights, medically, nutritionally, and developmentally, baby does not *need* an overnight feeding anymore. But again, the decision to continue with night feeding or wean your baby is up to you.

In the next month or two, you might notice that baby suddenly has nights when he wakes up three or four times. Sometimes this is simply from teething, so try to get a sense of whether or not he is in pain. I have many parents who bring in their children around this age for sleepless nights. Sometimes I find three to four teeth cutting through, or I may discover an ear infection or some other ailment to explain the overnight waking. Sometimes, though, there is nothing I can find wrong.

It seems that many babies just have a period of a few weeks when their sleep patterns shift and their schedules get off-kilter. I'm not sure scientifically why this happens, but it's very normal at this stage. Definitely take baby to see his doctor if he is having sudden spells of crying at night, just to be sure there is no cause for concern. If there is no specific cause for the waking, things should get back to normal in a few weeks or so.

Baby Safety

Baby proofing. Make life a little easier for your baby by making sure he has a clear path to move around, and try not to leave too many irresistible, breakable items lying around. I've often heard moms say that they won't change their home; they'll just teach baby what he can and can't touch. If you choose this option, be prepared for your baby to think his name is "No, no!" for a while as you correct him and divert his attention over and over again, daily. It's a whole lot easier on everyone to just get used to the fact that your living room will look like chaos for a few years. Put the glass vases and breakable picture frames on a high shelf. Or you can simply divide your home into safe and unsafe zones, allowing baby only to roam freely in truly safe areas of the house. You and your baby will both be a lot happier. Refer back to our simple baby-proofing checklist in Month Five for more ideas on creating a safe space for baby.

Expectations for Your Doctor Visits

Most pediatricians see babies around nine months of age for a well-baby checkup. This checkup typically does not include vaccines, though each doctor's schedule may differ slightly. If you have chosen to use an alternate vaccine schedule, this may be a good time to catch up on any immunizations your baby is lacking.

One of the most important aspects of the nine-month visit is to check for any signs of developmental delay. This will include checking carefully for delays in motor skills, speech development, and social development. Early signs of autism can be detected even at nine months of age, so it's important to let your doctor know if you've noticed any signs of delay. We will discuss more about early signs of autism in Month Twelve.

Your doctor will also weigh and measure your baby and make sure he is growing well. Parents are often concerned if baby's weight has not changed much since the last visit. Babies typically gain two pounds per month for the first few months, so at each checkup you have seen a big difference in weight. However, after six months of age, baby will typically gain only half a pound per month. It can be shocking to parents when they see that baby has only gained one or two pounds in the past three months, but this is normal and expected. Especially as baby learns to crawl and walk, he is going to start burning off calories, and those sweet little fat rolls will melt away as he starts to look more like a toddler. This is one of the visual reminders that baby is growing up.

Refer to Month Ten for more information about tests that may be administered in your nine-month well check.

Common Questions You May Have This Month

My baby is into everything! What is the best way to teach him what he can and cannot touch?

It depends on the situation. Be careful not to use the word "no" too much. If you say "No, no!" to every item he shouldn't touch, it will eventually lose its effectiveness. If he picks up something minor, like a paper you need, just gently take it away and give him something else. Items that can be dangerous (like electrical cords or stairwells) are much more risky and require a more serious response. It's important to let baby know what is off-limits, so a firm "No, no!" is fine. Stop him and calmly but firmly say, "No, don't touch." Then redirect his attention to something else that is okay to touch. Babies have short attention spans and short memories and can usually be distracted to a safe activity without tears. I do not recommend smacking hands or spanking. At this age, it just teaches them to hit and smack back.

My baby just got diagnosed with his third ear infection. Would it help if he got tubes in his ears?

This is a tough decision to make. Some children seem to have never-ending ear infections during the first year of life. Babies in day care and those exposed to cigarette smoke are particularly prone to ear infections and other common respiratory infections. Short-term complications of constant ear infections include pain, fever, and trouble sleeping. Babies with frequent ear infections can experience some speech delay as well. When babies constantly have fluid behind their eardrums, it's like they are hearing under water, and they do not properly hear language. Severe untreated ear infections can even cause damage to the eardrum itself.

For the most part, having three or four ear infections in the first year of life is acceptable. For babies who have resistant ear infections despite multiple antibiotics or those who develop delayed speech, ear tubes are a good option. Keep in mind that getting ear tubes does not eliminate infections—your child can still get upper respiratory infection and have a runny nose and ear drainage nearly every month. An ear, nose, and throat specialist can help you decide if ear tubes are right for your child. Ask your child's pediatrician if it's time for a referral.

A Real-Life Story

Having Babies Close Together

Kara Kae – mom to Jessika, Zoey, and Makenzi

I'll never forget the day I brought home my second daughter from the hospital. Her seventeen-month-old new-big-sister climbed in my lap while I was rocking the baby to sleep and wanted me to read her a book. "Wow, this is my life now."

The number one comment when I'm out with my kiddos is, "You've got your hands full, don't you?" I usually follow it with a blank stare and ask them to carry my groceries to the car for me. Or smile sweetly and remind them what a blessing my children are. People tend to forget that.

A man at the mall recently stopped me and stared down into the stroller with a huge look of shock on his face. "I can't believe there are TWO babies in there!!!" Seriously, dude? Did you think I had my cat in there?

It's almost like they feel sorry for me. WHY?? This was our choice, and it's amazing. I'm blessed with two tiny people who are absolutely incredible! My house is filled with laughter and fun. Sure, there are days my house looks like Babies R Us threw up and there are twelve dirty diapers laying on the living room floor. It's tough. I'm the first one to admit that. But most importantly . . . it's a blast. I wouldn't trade the bad days or the hard times for anything. Because when it's hard, *there's always a silver lining.*

Right when it gets really rough is when the baby giggles uncontrollably at her big sister for the first time. It's when your two-year-old says her Bible verse by herself, and sings her ABCs (skipping about ten letters, of course). It's when the big sister goes and sits next to her little sister and hugs and kisses her and tells her she loves her (without me telling her to!). Those moments make my eyes fill with tears and my heart fill with joy. They are learning from us! We are having a stinking blast teaching and loving these little humans. In no way does having my "hands full" change that.

Although having our kids really close together was our plan, sometimes it's a surprise. Whether you plan it or it's the shock of the century, it's a tough adjustment learning to juggle life with multiple little ones. My biggest advice to all moms, especially those with babies close together, is to give themselves grace, work to get on the same page with your husband, and don't even attempt to do it all. Have a goal for each day. Some days my goal is to only focus on my girls. Some days my goal is to unload the dishwasher or do a load of laundry. These are not lofty goals. As a mom of little ones, I have to give grace to myself when the house is a mess at the end of the day. Because we are on the same page, my husband understands and is happy to relax with me while the dishes wait until tomorrow. It's tough enough just to manage it all, so I don't even try to perfect it all. As long as I have a happy family, then I'm content with a job well done.

Soon I will bring my third baby home from the hospital and I can't wait to have all three of them in my lap to read a story. Because these hands-full moments are what it's all about.

Truth for the Journey

"You show that you are a letter from Christ, the result of our ministry, written not with ink but with the Spirit of the living God, not on tablets of stone but on tablets of human hearts. Such confidence we have through Christ before God. Not that we are competent in ourselves to claim anything for ourselves, but our competence comes from God." 2 Corinthians 3:3–5

If I haven't expressed it clearly enough in previous chapters, I want to affirm you: you are doing a great job. You are a good mom. You are the perfect mom for your sweet baby. Do you believe that? Baby's first year is full of exciting adventures and milestones, but it's a journey traveled on uncharted waters for many (especially if this is your first baby). I'd be surprised if you cruised through the first twelve months of your child's life without encountering doubt and feelings of failure.

One thing I hear very often from the moms in our community is that they need to be affirmed and assured that they are a "good mom." While I understand the need—and share it—I wonder who is qualified to define the term "good mom." Think about it. What is "good" to one may be "mediocre" to some. What is "okay" to one may be "stellar" to others. We so easily fall into the trap of comparing ourselves to other moms and feeling like we fall short as we seek their approval. But we cannot rate our mothering ability against the standards or practices of other moms. We should not compare that which cannot be tangibly measured.

"I am a little pencil in the hand of a writing God who is sending a love letter to the world" (attributed to Mother Teresa).

I came across this quote recently and began to picture myself and my children as little pencils in God's hand writing a letter. *What does it say?* I've wondered. If God is writing a letter with my life or my child's life, who am I to tell him how to write it? Who am I to compare what he is writing for us with what he is writing for another? Because our letters or our stories are a unique part of his master plan, ours will look different than others. Comparing ourselves to those around us is a painful waste of our thoughts and our time.

In 2 Corinthians, Paul explains to the church in Corinth that they are living letters of Christ, written not on tablets of stone but on "tablets of human hearts." This word, along with the poignant thoughts of Mother Teresa, is a powerful picture of the testimony of our lives. When we envision our Father God writing a unique story with our life firmly planted as a writing instrument in his steady hand, we will no longer measure our successes or failures against another person. We can trust that he is guiding us through every new experience with love and grace—that all things will work together for good.

In 2 Corinthians 3:4, Paul reveals the source of such confident trust. "Such confidence we have through Christ before God. Not that we are competent in ourselves . . . but our competence comes from God." How many times have you felt incompetent as a mother in the past nine months? Dozens, I'm sure. I know that's how I felt and still feel from time to time. But we are reminded through this verse of a truth we all know deep down in our hearts. Our confidence and our ability come from God, not ourselves. You can be sure you are a good mom because your competence comes from Christ. As you walk daily with him, your every effort will not only be good enough, it will be great.

Another area in which you may be tempted to compare yourself to other moms is your appearance. How many times have you looked at a mom from your birthing class or playgroup who had her baby around the same time as you and thought, "Gosh, she looks so thin. I'm still carrying around fifteen pounds of this baby weight" or "How does she have time to make herself look so put together? I barely have time to shower!"? I get it. I do it, too (even eighteen months after having my baby). But once again, this trap is a painful waste of our thoughts and our time. Just like we cannot compare our stories to other moms, we cannot compare our bodies and our lifestyles. If you notice that another mom has worked hard and gotten the weight off, then ask her to share what worked, but keep in mind that it may not work the same for you. If you love the way another mom dresses with seemingly little effort, ask her the secret to her "look." While it's okay to seek advice and camaraderie from friends as you look to find ways to care for yourself, do not let yourself fall into the comparison trap.

Dr. Rupe and I shared some tips in earlier chapters about ways to get back into shape after baby. Go back and review that encouragement and ask the Lord to help you get back on track if you've fallen off. Just as your ability to care for your baby comes from the Lord, so does your ability and the grace to care for yourself. Remember that you are beautifully and wonderfully made by a loving God. Your physical makeup is perfectly unique according to his plan. This might mean you have to work a bit harder or smarter, but he will guide you through a plan that works for you because he desires for you to be healthy and at peace with your appearance.

Your Marriage

We've talked about marriage a few times throughout the book because your marriage is one of the most important foundations of your child's life. Continue to work hard to connect with your spouse on a regular basis. Consider a weekly or twice-monthly date night to get away and spend time alone. Try not to talk just about the baby when you have quiet moments to chat. Talk about each other, your dreams, and your walk with the Lord. Talk close friends or family members into doing a babysitting swap so you can have date night on a regular basis without breaking the bank on child care costs.

Date Night Discussion Starters

1. What challenges are you facing at work right now? (Many husbands do not talk about work after baby comes because they feel like it's unimportant compared to the baby. But your spouse needs support. Ask him about his job.)

2. When baby is old enough to be left with his grandparents, where would you like to go on a trip? (Dream about future kid-free vacations!)

3. Is there a hobby you'd like to pursue (or continue) now that we're getting into a groove with baby? (Both mom and dad need something fun to challenge them.)

4. Once we put away all these baby books, what book would you like to read . . . for fun? (Maybe find something you can read and discuss together.)

5. Are there any ministries in church you'd like to get involved in now that baby is comfortable in the nursery? (Now might be a great time to get plugged in to your church body.)

Sowing the seeds of time and focus into your marriage will reap great benefits in the months to come. I pray you are able to connect on a deeper level now that you've created life together. Your baby is the fruit of your marriage, your union. Be mindful of this and continue to water the roots of your family.

Leaving Baby with a Sitter

Whether you leave your baby with a family member or official babysitter, make sure that person is prepared for anything. Organize baby's food, diaper supplies, clothes, and toys so your sitter will be able to find everything baby needs. Leave important contact numbers and instructions in an easy-to-find place, such as the fridge or kitchen counter. Don't forget to include the numbers for poison control and your baby's doctor. If for some reason your sitter cannot reach you immediately, he or she should be able to contact help in an emergency. When taking baby to a caregiver's house, make sure to pack extra supplies, clothes, and food. If you will be out for an extended period of time (two or more hours), check in with your sitter to make sure things are going smoothly.

A Note for Single Moms

We've purposed to consider moms from all walks of life in this book. If you are a single mom, this discussion about marriage might be hard for you. If you have the desire to be married, mama, then believe with your whole heart that God will provide a wonderful husband for you in his perfect timing. The Word says, "He places the lonely in families" (Ps. 68:6 NLT). When he provides the partner you desire, all of these truths will apply to your growing family. In the meantime, lean into the Lord for continued strength and wisdom. No matter what the circumstances surrounding your situation, he loves you deeply and will provide everything you and your baby need. I am always amazed by the strength and grace of single moms. Be proud of the way you have cared for your baby this year, my friend. It is a testament to your strength and your love for your child.

As I think about a mother's state of mind around this time of baby's first year, I am reminded of the sweet quote from the movie *The Help*. "You is kind, you is smart, you is important." I feel we need a similar mantra of encouragement as moms.

When you feel overwhelmed and discouraged, I hope you will be reminded—you is wise, you is loving, you is a good mama!

Prayer Concerns

Baby's language development

Baby's mobility

Getting back into shape

My marriage

A Prayer for This Month

Dear Lord,

Thank you for the amazing reward of hearing my baby utter words and sounds. I pray that you would guide his language development. As I work toward getting back into shape, give me grace, Lord, to make the right choices and find time to take care of myself. Cover my marriage and help us find strategies to communicate and connect in the midst of the busyness. I know that our family is only as strong as my relationship with my husband. Thank you for the gift that he is to our family. Amen.

Write your own prayer of reflection.

_____

_____

_____

_____

Journal

_____

_____

_____

_____

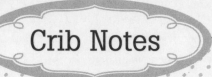

Crib Notes

Months Seven to Nine

Mommy's Heart—Do not compare yourself or your baby to others. You are doing a great job and your baby is growing wonderfully. Remember, your confidence comes from Christ, not from others (2 Cor. 3:4–5).

Baby's Development—Baby is beginning to sit up and may begin to crawl during this stage. He may also stand with support or begin to cruise. He's babbling more and may begin uttering consonant sounds soon. His separation anxiety is developing now.

Feeding—Breastfeeding: 15 to 30 minutes four times per day. Bottle-feeding: 6 to 8 ounces four times per day. Baby will take milk between his newly introduced "meal times" now that he is eating solid foods.

Sleeping—9 to 12 hours at night with two 30-minute to 2-hour naps.

Play—Ask your baby, "What does a cow say?" and teach him the appropriate animal response. Stack blocks in front of your baby and watch him try to knock them over. Applaud baby enthusiastically when he engages in play. He will love the affirmation.

Cruising Along

Baby Stats

By ten months, babies range from 16.3 to 24.5 pounds (7.4–11.2 kg) in weight and approximately 27.5 to 30.5 inches (69–77 cm) in length.

Development Checker at Ten Months

Typical Skills

- ❏ Can creep, scoot, or crawl
- ❏ May be able to pull to stand and cruise around furniture
- ❏ Shakes, bangs, and throws objects
- ❏ Feeds self with fingers
- ❏ Crude pincer grasp
- ❏ Can drink from a cup
- ❏ May be able to point at objects
- ❏ Shows interest in his surroundings
- ❏ May be able to wave bye-bye or play peekaboo
- ❏ Recognizes own name (i.e., turns to look if name is called)
- ❏ Understands several words
- ❏ Able to babble and imitate sounds
- ❏ May say "mama" or "dada," but not yet specific to own mother or father

Concerning Signs

- ❏ Unable to push up on hands and knees
- ❏ No attempt to babble or make consonant sounds
- ❏ Doesn't like "social" games like peek-a-boo

Language

Read to your child every day. Choose books with bright, simple pictures. Your baby will have a short attention span for now and may not be able to finish an entire book. In fact, he may just want to chew on the book more than anything else. He may enjoy pointing out objects in the pictures rather than reading the actual story. Resist the feeling that you need to read every page in order. Allow baby to turn to the pages that interest him most.

Talking to baby will help lay the foundation for language. Repeatedly name objects and describe to him what you're doing while you cook, clean, dress, and play. This will help build up his vocabulary dramatically as he begins to talk.

Minimizing television exposure is important to baby's language development. Children at this age need *active* interaction and play. The AAP recommends complete avoidance of television exposure until age two. Babies learn language and social interaction best from a real person, not from a TV (no matter how "educational" the content). If baby is engrossed with the TV, you are far less likely to be talking to him and interacting with him. Because this face-to-face interaction is so important, the AAP takes a strong stance. For many families, this is not a recommendation that is easily followed. In most homes, it is not reasonable to expect that baby can avoid hearing or seeing any television for the first two years. If you do allow baby to have television exposure, keep it minimal, age appropriate, and educational. Remember, baby's brain is a sponge, and he is soaking up whatever he sees and hears.

Movement

At this point, your home should be well baby proofed, at least in the most-used areas such as baby's room, the kitchen, and the living room. Your child is going to be on the move soon. Whether by crawling or cruising, he will love exploring the house like never before. All of those things that he has seen for the past nine months he will now be able to get to and touch. Watch out for safety hazards such as phone and electrical cords, long curtains, and window blinds and cords. Use gates at the top and bottom of stairs to prevent falls. We discourage the use of infant walkers, as these can allow your child to access potential safety hazards and may delay the skills needed for walking.

Many parents will ask about the best kind of shoes for their baby once he starts pulling up. Babies learn to walk by balancing on their feet and gripping their toes on the ground. So, learning to walk barefoot is best for most babies. Whether or not your baby has on shoes will probably not affect how quickly he learns to walk. If you are concerned about his feet being cold, or if the flooring in your home makes walking difficult, choose a shoe with flexible soles. Because the arches in babies' feet are flexible and don't develop until they are toddlers, your baby shouldn't need shoes with special arch support. Your baby will probably outgrow his shoes every two or three months, so measure his feet regularly to make sure he is in the proper size.

A Note about Baby Walkers

Baby walkers, a once common piece of baby gear, are quickly losing popularity. A traditional, old-school baby walker has wheels on the bottom and should not be confused with the more current, stationary ExerSaucer (which when used properly should provide no harm to baby). Though many parents believe a baby walker will help their baby learn to walk, the opposite may be true. There are no known benefits to using a walker, and using one frequently may actually delay walking in some babies. There is a fairly high risk of injury with baby walkers, especially in homes with stairs. Remember, it is not necessarily a good thing for baby to be able to get anywhere in the house he wants to go! If you choose to use a baby walker, your baby must be closely supervised at all times. Never leave baby alone while he is in a baby walker.

Social Interaction

Discipline. Believe it or not, you have reached the stage where it is important to start discipline. Now that your baby is beginning to be mobile, you will have to closely monitor his surroundings for hazards. Hopefully you have baby proofed your home to the best of your ability, but your sweet little darling will still find something to get into. Once your baby is crawling and walking, safety will be of the utmost importance, and certain things (such as the stove) will be off-limits. These "No, no!" areas in your home will become less attractive to your baby with consistency on your part. If your child gets near something that is hazardous, firmly tell him no and redirect him to a different safe object or activity. After a few weeks of getting the same reaction from you every time, he will learn.

Natural consequences are another good way to discipline at this age. If your child continues to purposefully throw his cereal despite being told no, he will soon see that there is no more cereal on his tray. Resist the urge to give him more right away just because he fusses. Encourage him to eat something else on his tray instead. This gentle form of discipline will help him learn consequences as well as patience.

Baby Care
Feeding

Your baby should continue to receive either breast milk or iron-fortified formula as his main source of nutrition. Whole milk should not be given until after your child is twelve months old. Most nine-month-olds drink between 20 and 30 ounces per day. If your baby is drinking less than 16 ounces per day or more than 36 ounces per day, your doctor may have you add more solids into his diet. If your baby is exclusively breastfed or is getting less than 33 ounces of formula a day, he will still need a vitamin D supplement daily.

Work on introducing your baby to a sippy cup at this age. Juice is not necessary, but if given it should be diluted with water and amount to no more than 6 ounces per day. Don't be fooled into thinking that by drinking juice, your baby is getting a serving of fruit. Juice is basically sugar water. It is a good idea, though, to start introducing water through a sippy cup so your child can begin to learn the skills needed to drink from a cup.

Finger foods. Foods with more texture can be introduced now. Your baby may be ready for Stage 3 foods, which have small, soft chunks in them. You can try a variety of table foods as well, as long as they are soft and not a choking hazard. Once your baby can sit up well and bring his hands to his mouth, he is ready to learn to feed himself. His pincer grasp should be getting better, and he may be able to pick up small puffs and cereal, small pieces of banana, or soft crackers. Do not give him any foods that would require chewing. Think outside the box when feeding your baby. You may discover that he loves the taste of hummus or guacamole, for example. These are both very soft and nutritious and are commonly on the menu in restaurants. Again, there is no medical data that suggests withholding foods containing eggs or peanut butter will prevent allergies later on, though some parents still like to avoid these until after baby is one. Avoid honey until after the first birthday due to the risk of infantile botulism exposure. Also avoid choking hazards such as nuts, raw vegetables, and round slices of food (e.g., hot dogs).

Don't force your child to finish every bite of food on his plate. If he is turning his head away and pushing the spoon back away from him, he is done and shouldn't be forced to continue eating. Avoid mealtime battles now to help prevent him from disliking sitting at the table with your family. This will make mealtime more pleasant now and in the future.

Continue to brush your child's teeth after meals and before bedtime. Toothpastes with fluoride should be avoided until after your baby can spit. Your doctor may recommend a fluoride supplement, however, depending on the water in your area.

Sleep and Schedules

Continue to have consistent nap times and bedtime. Children at this age still usually need two naps a day, often one of those naps being two to three hours long. Encourage him to sleep in his own crib. Be sure to lower the crib mattress now that he can pull to stand.

Baby Safety

Choking. If your baby is choking and you are able to see the food in his mouth, use your finger to sweep the food clear from the mouth. If his choking appears to be worse, especially if baby is blue or looks unresponsive, first and foremost someone should call 911. Back blows and chest thrusts per CPR guidelines can then be initiated. For back blows, first sit down and then hold the infant face down across your forearm (forearm should be resting on your thigh, baby tilted down). Then give five firm back blows with the heel of your hand. This technique, as well as proper chest thrusts, are typically covered in an infant CPR class, making it that much more important that you complete the class to help you in the event your baby chokes on a piece of food.

Car seat. Your child is still rear-facing in his car seat at this age. State laws may allow babies to be turned front-facing after their first birthday if they meet weight requirements. However, current AAP recommendations suggest that it is safest for your child to stay rear-facing until age two. Do watch closely for the weight limit on your child's car seat. Many infant carrier (bucket) car seats only support up to 23 pounds. Your child may need the next stage (convertible) car seat, still rear-facing, soon.

Expectations for Your Doctor Visits

There is no scheduled visit with the pediatrician this month. If your child has missed any immunizations along the way, or if you are using an alternate vaccine schedule, this is a good time to catch up. Remember, the longer you wait to vaccinate, the longer your baby is unprotected from serious illnesses.

Sometime between nine and twelve months old, your baby's pediatrician will check him for anemia through a simple heel prick or blood draw. Babies naturally have a dip in their hemoglobin around this age and can become anemic. Most babies will soon be transitioning from iron-rich breast milk or formula to regular cow's milk (which is low in iron). Your child's pediatrician will make sure his level does not dip too low in preparation for this transition. If baby does have anemia, your pediatrician may prescribe an iron supplement and recheck his labs in a few months. If there is any history of anemia in your family, be sure to inform his doctor.

Your child's doctor may also screen him for lead poisoning sometime between nine and twelve months. The most common source of lead exposure is lead-based paint. Your child can be exposed to lead-based paint that is chipping inside the home or in the dirt surrounding a home that was painted with lead-based paint. If you live in a home built before 1978, there is a chance that it may have lead-based paint, and you should have the home tested. Lead can also be found in water running through old pipes, in certain hobby materials such as solder and stained glass, or even in older ceramic dishes or mini blinds. Lead poisoning usually occurs slowly, as it builds up in the bloodstream. Common signs of lead poisoning in older children include learning disabilities and behavior problems. Severe cases can lead to brain damage that may be irreversible. Lead poisoning is treatable and is most successful when caught early. If you have any concerns that your child could be exposed to lead, make sure you tell your doctor.

Your pediatrician has long been on the lookout for any signs of developmental delay. This is a particularly important time to start looking for any signs of autism. Your doctor will discuss with you some of the early warning signs of this condition. See Month Twelve for more on the early indicators of autism.

Common Questions You May Have This Month

My baby is more interested in baby food and juice than in his milk. How can I be sure he's getting enough?

This is a common concern for many parents. In order for baby to have the amount of iron and other vitamins and nutrients he needs, it is recommended that he receive at least 16 ounces of breast milk or iron-fortified formula daily. Many parents grow concerned that their baby "won't" drink milk and instead prefers juices. (This is yet another reason to delay starting juice.) Baby is learning preferences, and though he cannot talk in words, he can definitely let you know his opinions. If your baby is going on "strike" against milk, a little perseverance and tough love on your part may be in order. First of all, stop the juice. He is not going to get dehydrated if he doesn't drink for several hours. Offer milk during meals. This is a great way to get in an extra cup or so of milk per day. Try a different cup. The novelty of a new sippy cup or a straw may entice him to drink more milk as well. If you have any concerns about his nutrition, talk to his pediatrician for additional recommendations.

My baby is breastfed and has no interest in trying a sippy cup. How can I help him with this transition?

Both breastfed and bottle-fed babies may resist the transition of receiving their milk (or other liquids) in a different form. My own son had a very hard time transitioning to a cup despite being bottle-fed. There are numerous kinds of cups you can try (including soft silicone spouts, hard plastic spouts, and those with straws). You may end up buying all three in an attempt to find which will work best. Just buy one at a time and see how it goes before you invest in an arsenal of any one particular type. Your baby will probably not figure it out on the first attempt. You have to keep offering the cup over and over. Be patient. He will eventually figure it out. Keep in mind, there's no law that says baby *has* to be off of a bottle or breast by twelve months. Using a cup now is just for practice.

Truth for the Journey

"The precepts of the Lord are right, giving joy to the heart. The commands of the Lord are radiant, giving light to the eyes." Psalm 19:8

Can you believe your baby is almost ten months old, and we've already used the word "discipline" in this book? I know, I know. You were hoping to reach his eighteenth birthday and send him off to college without ever having to correct his sweet, little angel heart. Wouldn't that be nice? Inevitably, as your baby's personality and will develop, he will begin to test his limits. This means that you have to be ready to correct and lead him. Dr. Johnston gave some great tips on ways to gently discipline your little one when he gets into something that could be harmful. It's important to understand (and this may make you feel better when thinking about "disciplining" your sweet baby) that your little one does not yet know right from wrong; therefore, you are not necessarily correcting bad behavior as much as you are teaching him what is permissible and not permissible. As he learns basic cause and effect, he needs to be able to apply that understanding to his own actions. Ultimately, your purpose is twofold—protecting him and gaining his trust.

It may sit better with your heart, mama, to look at this practice as guiding your soon-to-be toddler's heart. The key verse this month from Psalms shares the benefits of following your Heavenly Father: joy for your heart and light for your eyes.

In this same way, you are laying a foundation for your child to understand similar benefits that come from trusting and obeying his parents.

My little man has just entered the toddler stage. He has been mobile for months and is like the Tasmanian devil exploring various rooms in our home since I put away the baby gates. Just yesterday he discovered the buffet in my dining room where I store all of my candleholders. Many of these treasures are glass. Despite my diligent efforts to redirect him every time he approaches, he continues to make a move for this forbidden corner of our house once an hour (it seems). I have noticed his will getting stronger and stronger the more I firmly say "No, no!" and remove him from the room. He cries and kicks his feet to let me know he is not pleased with these limits. Despite his obvious disapproval, I cannot waver from affirming this limitation, or he could hurt himself or, worse, come to think he rules the castle.

Just as our obedience to the Lord's precepts gives joy to our hearts, so our child's obedience will bring joy to his. And just as our understanding of the commands of the Lord brings light to our eyes, so does our child's understanding bring light to his own. Believe it or not, mama, now is the time to lay a foundation of obedience in your child's life. You may not actually see him acting out of his will for another few months, but as he becomes more and more independent, his curiosity and desire to do his own thing will grow. You need to take baby steps with your child into the toddler season.

While we are meditating on this verse, I want to stop and consider how it can encourage us as we ask the Lord for wisdom for the coming months. "The commands of the Lord are radiant, giving light to the eyes." You may feel like you are in the dark once again as you look toward the toddler stage. Your once tiny and cuddly little one is about to enter a whole new stage of growth, activity, and experience. Once again, you will need desperately to look to the Lord for wisdom at every turn. The decisions you've made up until this point in baby's life have been mostly on temporary issues. Breast versus bottle, cloth versus disposable diapers, strict schedule versus flexible routine—all of these determinations are for a short period of time. The crossroads you come to at this point in your child's life will require long-term decision making. What food will he eat? Will I limit sugar or not allow it at all? What about media? TV or no TV? iPad or no iPad? (And no, I am not joking.

Your child will feel the gravitational pull of your tablet and phone very soon.) You've heard the saying, "Start as you mean to go on." The boundaries you set in these areas will follow you into the preschool years and beyond. Of course, you can always regroup, but it's a lot easier said than done. Therefore, as you begin thinking forward to the near future for your baby, grab hold of this promise that the commands of the Lord give light to the eyes. As you honor him and the role he's called you to in your child's life, he will illuminate your mind on every issue you face.

Balancing Baby's Exploration

Your baby's ability to move is developing daily. Before you know it, he will be all over the place. This is such a sweet time as you see him exploring his surroundings. But it can also be unnerving as he goes places he's never gone before. Moms need to find the delicate balance between presenting boundaries and opportunities to explore for their baby. Much of this depends on your home environment.

I just read an article on the Internet (yes, I do read the Internet, although I have and always will strongly caution moms against putting too much stock in it—and this story is a case in point, so bear with me) entitled something like, "Why I Won't Put My Baby in a Play Pen." The mom (of one ten-month-old, mind you) went on and on about how she does not believe in keeping her child contained . . . how she wants to encourage his freedom and teach him boundaries. Several moms chimed in on the conversation and commented that they too do not believe in play pens or "baby jails" that limit their little ones and fail to teach them boundaries. While I understand the desire to teach your child early on what he can and cannot touch, I think this debate is largely dependent on the individual baby. Some kids seem more content to sit and play and, left to their own devices, will not destroy your living room or injure themselves on the remains of your favorite vase. My children, as I mentioned earlier, are more curious and inquisitive and are not satisfied if there is an unexplored inch in the room. For some moms, using a playpen (or play yard) is the only way she'll get to go to the bathroom throughout the day.

Play yards designate a space for safe play. There are many options for this designated space, including your trusty Pack 'N Play. These dual-use tools tend to be a bit smaller, so I would recommend, if you are going to leave baby in this safe space for longer periods of time, that you invest in a larger play yard or baby gate. Do some research and find one that will work well in your space. Clear the area of decorative items, frames, or other things baby can grab, and fill it with toys, books, and objects he is allowed to touch and chew. You may find he becomes frustrated in this environment the more mobile he gets. Don't be too quick to post your gates on Craigslist, though. He may need to fuss through until he becomes more comfortable with his space.

I finally removed our baby gate when I got tired of climbing over it and wanted my living room back. Our baby was beginning to walk and definitely wanted more space to roam. Although he might seem to need more boundaries at that point rather than fewer, we decided to remove the gates and expect him to learn what he can and cannot touch around the house. This has required much more attention on my part, but we felt it was time. Since babies crawl, cruise, and walk at very different ages between seven and fifteen months of age, your timeline may look very different than ours. The key is to find the right balance of boundaries and exploration that works well for you, your baby, and your environment. No matter how you set up his surroundings, simply make sure the space is baby proofed for greater safety. If you have older children in the house, keep toys with lots of pieces and smaller objects out of baby's space and possibly stored in sealed boxes out of reach. Do not depend on your older children to keep small objects out of baby's reach. They will need help storing and managing their toys.

As with many other points of practicality in baby's first year, there is no right or wrong when it comes to this issue. If you do not like the idea of keeping your baby contained in a specific space, then by all means, let him roam. Just make sure your space is well baby proofed before you do.

I pray that your eyes will be enlightened on every question you have and every decision you face during this formative stage in baby's first year. Once again, be reminded that all the wisdom you need for your baby is available at a moment's notice as you ask the Lord for guidance. You can rest assured that he will answer every call.

Prayer Concerns

Safety for baby as he moves about

Mobile development

Early discipline

Wisdom with boundaries

A Prayer for This Month

Dear Lord,

What an exciting time this is . . . seeing my baby move around so much. But it's also a bit unnerving. Give me wisdom to create boundaries for my child. Protect him as he moves about. When it comes time to administer discipline to establish boundaries and keep him safe, I ask for your grace in each moment. Enlighten my heart, Lord, to understand the need for this guidance, as unpleasant as it may be. I want to be obedient to you in leading my child. Amen.

Write your own prayer of reflection.

_____

_____

_____

_____

_____

Journal

_____

_____

_____

_____

_____

Becoming a Toddler

Baby Stats

By eleven months, babies range from 16.75 to 25.5 pounds (7.6–11.6 kg) in weight and approximately 27.5 to 31 inches (70–79 cm) in length.

Development Checker at Eleven Months

Typical Skills
- ❏ Plays games such as patty-cake and peekaboo
- ❏ Pulls to stand
- ❏ Cruises well
- ❏ Stands alone for a few seconds
- ❏ Says "mama" or "dada" to the correct parent

Concerning Signs
- ❏ Does not crawl
- ❏ Cannot stand when supported

Language

At this stage, babies are typically able to speak one or two words. For most babies, these are usually "mama" and "dada." Some babies may be able to say "baba" or "bye-bye." Don't be alarmed if your baby cannot say both "mama" and "dada" yet. To the parent who is still waiting to hear their name, the wait is excruciating! But it will come—just give it time. Baby may also start to have some inflection in his voice and try to imitate adult speech patterns. He will soon learn the art of a two-way conversation. Listen when baby babbles and squeals to you, and then say something back. He'll probably wait until you are done speaking and then respond again.

It will be many more months before you know the deep thoughts he's sharing, but it's fun nonetheless.

Baby understands much more than he can say. If you are talking about his blanket or a favorite toy, he can probably scan the room and find it. Keep talking to him throughout the day. Describe to him what you're doing. "Watch mommy wash the dishes. Look at all the bubbles. The water is hot!" He is watching you and listening always. By naming items as you work, you will help him pick up on new words and expand his vocabulary.

Baby may begin to develop his own words for things soon. For example, he may decide to say "bob" when referring to his bottle or sippy cup. If he uses the word consistently, it will help with communication frustrations, and you will learn to identify what he is asking for. Avoid saying his made-up word back to him, though. When you hand him the cup, make sure to say "cup," so he eventually learns the proper word.

You may be interested in trying sign language to help with communication. Babies who sign typically develop speech more quickly and have less frustration than babies who are unable to communicate. Even if it's just three or four signs that you learn with baby, it may make a huge impact on daily living. We taught my son just a few simple signs: more, all done, and milk. What a difference! He could finally tell us what he wanted at mealtimes, which then became more fun. There are many resources available for teaching your baby sign language. Find one that works well for you and remember to only attempt to teach baby two to three signs at a time. Most families end up using only four to five signs routinely.

Some parents are concerned that their child has a speech delay if he is not saying several words by now. Try not to compare your child with other children who might be advanced for their age. Remember, we only expect babies to say one or two words by their first birthday.

There are two common types of speech delay: expressive and receptive. Expressive speech delay is much more common. With expressive speech delay, a child is able to understand what is being spoken to him, but he cannot respond back with words. For example, if you start talking about a cookie, he knows exactly what you are talking about. He may even walk over to the cookie and point at it or even pick it up if he is able. He is processing language just fine, even if he can't actually say the word "cookie." In receptive speech delay, a child is not able to understand language and gestures as well as expected for his age. Receptive language understanding typically develops prior to expressive language development. Therefore, it's common for children who have receptive language delay to also have expressive language delay.

Although some patience is required when waiting for baby's speech to develop, always trust your instinct as a parent if you are concerned that he is delayed. You may hear friends or family offer reassurances like "He's just a late bloomer," or "My grandson talked late and now he won't be quiet—give it time." While these reassurances may be true, never feel uneasy about bringing up concerns for speech or developmental delays with your child's pediatrician. Early intervention has been proven to give better outcomes in children with developmental delays. Your child's doctor can refer him to a speech pathologist or other early intervention program for a full evaluation. If he sees a speech pathologist and passes with flying colors, then all the better—at least you will be reassured.

(Resource on this topic include healthychildren.org.)

Developing a Love for Books

As we've mentioned before, reading is one of the best ways to develop your child's language skills. Snuggling with your baby on your lap and looking at books is also a wonderful bonding experience. He will love to hear the sound of your voice and will associate reading with comfort and happy memories. Children who learn to love books at a young age typically enjoy school and have better grades than their peers who were not read to. If you haven't already, look for programs in your area such as Dolly Parton's Imagination Library that will send your child free books. These programs are there to help parents nurture a love of reading in their child. Take advantage of your local library as well. Attend story time regularly, as this activity will provide social interaction for your soon-to-be toddler as well as the chance for you to get out and meet other moms.

(Reach Out and Read, ROR, December 2012. Retrieved from http://www.reachoutandread.org/FileRepository/PolicyCaseForROR.pdf)

Movement

Your little one is still developing his pincer grasp at this stage. This will make it much easier for him to pick up finger foods from his high chair tray. Most babies have mastered the art of a scissor grasp by now—picking up objects between their thumb and side of their hand—although you'll want to keep actual scissors far out of reach for some time. Baby may also start pointing at objects he is interested in or poking at his food with just his index finger. These little steps are all part of baby's development of fine motor skills.

Your baby is on the move, mama! He can easily get from lying down to a sitting position without assistance, then scoot, creep, or crawl to whatever he can get his hands on. He is probably starting to pull to stand as well (and maybe even taking a few steps), which brings on a whole new set of challenges. This is a good time to reassess your baby proofing. Make sure there are no tablecloths or curtains or loose pieces of fabric that could be hazardous if baby decides to use them to pull to stand.

Once baby can pull to stand, he'll start cruising along walls and furniture. He may even let go and stand for a few seconds. Some babies take their first steps now. Keep the camera ready so you don't miss it. Try not to worry if other children his age are walking and your child is not. Your baby is not behind—the other children are just a little ahead. It's completely normal if your baby doesn't take any steps for a few more months. Some children are a little more timid than others and take their time in learning to walk.

Social Interaction

Separation anxiety. Your baby may be at the peak of stranger anxiety or separation anxiety at this point. Be reassured that this is a normal stage of development, even for children who end up being independent social butterflies. Give your child daily periods of physical contact to affirm his sense of security. Hold him and read books together or just cuddle and rock before bed for an extended period. Cherish these times while he is still little enough to want to let you hug on him. It won't be too many years before he's too cool for that (or at least he'll say he is).

Socializing your baby. Many moms, especially stay-at-home moms, are concerned that their baby is not getting enough social time with other babies at this point. At eleven to twelve months, one-on-one time, which encourages security for your baby, is of more importance. Socialization with other children can occur in small bursts at church, your local library's story time, music classes, and so on. Although you may be anxious to teach your baby to share (especially if he has older siblings in the home), babies still play independently at this stage. They cannot yet understand the concept of sharing because they don't co-play. What will be helpful is to start teaching "please," "thank you," and "you're welcome." Anytime baby hands you something, you should cheerfully say "thank you!"—he'll learn to like the reaction he gets from you and begin to understand this important social give and take.

Baby Care
Feeding

At this point, any solid food that is not a choking hazard is fair game for baby. Be sure to offer him a food even if you don't care for it. He may learn to love beets, for example, despite the fact that you and your spouse don't. Offer him interesting new things at restaurants that he might not ordinarily get at home to expand his palate for different flavors. If baby turns his nose up at something, don't be afraid to try it again later. You will find (especially when baby is one or two years old) that his favorite food one day may be the food he spits out the next day. Just keep offering healthy foods and avoid the pitfall of only offering one or two foods he likes just for the sake of getting him to eat.

Overall, you will find on some days that baby will eat much less now than he did as a six- or seven-month-old. This is often confusing and frustrating for parents. Try to keep in mind that this behavior is normal and expected for this age. Baby's growth is not as rapid now as it was in the past few months. If you looked at a growth chart, you would see that the expected growth curve flattens out and slows down at this stage. He doesn't need the same hearty quantity of daily calories as he needed just a few months ago. Plus, there are many more distractions for baby now, and you will find that he'd rather play than eat much of the time. This is also completely natural at this stage, so there is no need to "force" your baby to eat a certain amount.

Sleep and Schedules

Your baby is likely in a pretty good routine at this point. His schedule is more predictable, and hopefully he's a good sleeper. If your baby is still waking up at night, it may be hard to know how to handle it. There are certainly many schools of thought on this. Some experts strongly support the "cry it out" method. Others say that you should attend to baby's needs every time, right away, because crying can stress him out. I think the right answer for most parents is somewhere in the middle. As discussed earlier in the book, there is a difference between "fussing" it out and "crying" it out. If baby is in bed at night and wakes up squirming and fussing, it may be appropriate to give him some time to see if he'll lie back down on his own. Certainly, if baby is screaming and seems inconsolable, most parents can't ignore this, and it's probably best to go and comfort him quickly.

Baby can sit up now and probably pull to stand easily. He's also very smart. He *knows* what pushes your buttons. If you come running every time he makes even a little squeak, he's going to know he can get your attention easily. However, it's hard to ignore a baby who is standing and holding the crib railing and screaming "Mama!" Try to assess if he really needs something or is just trying to get your attention. Reassure him and give him a transitional object that he associates with sleep. Avoid giving him milk in the middle of the night. Very few babies need overnight feedings at this point. It's a bad habit to continue now that he has teeth, since having milk on the teeth all night can lead to cavities.

Baby Safety

Baby falls. Baby may be walking now, though not very well. It will be many months before he is stable, so expect lots of falls at this stage. You can guarantee that your baby will fall and hit his head as he is learning and after he starts walking, probably multiple times a day. I often joke with parents (mostly parents of boys) that this is why God gave babies hard heads. In all seriousness though, it's scary to see your infant whack his head on the floor or on furniture. Thankfully, the maternal fear is usually worse than the actual bump on the head. For minor head injuries, you can expect that baby may cry and need comforting for a few minutes. He'll usually then go right back to playing as he was before. He may develop a bruise or a knot on his head at the site of the injury. It's important to be aware of signs that his injury could be more serious. Certainly, if he loses consciousness—gets "knocked out"—he should be seen by a doctor right away. He may also seem irritable if the head injury is serious, especially if he acts this way for more than ten or fifteen minutes. Other signs that a head injury could be serious are that he seems overly sleepy during his usual wakeful hours or that you are unable to wake him from sleep. When in doubt, call your doctor immediately.

Outdoor play. Since baby is newly or almost mobile, you may find it more challenging now to play outside. He will want to crawl or scoot around, and you may not be comfortable with him roaming in the grass or on the sidewalk. Your limitations will depend on your surroundings. If you have a nice yard or perhaps live on a cul-de-sac, you can probably allow your baby to play outside. Make sure you keep a close eye on him and never be more than a hand's reach away at any time. If your baby is walking already, he is still clumsy and can easily take a spill and end up with scraped hands or a big knot on his head from the sidewalk. You may instead want to go for a walk and push him in a stroller. He'll still love being outside to see and hear interesting new things. Take him to the park and push him in a baby swing. Babies like to people-watch, so he'll love hearing other children laugh and play.

Expectations for Your Doctor Visits

There are no regularly scheduled doctor's visits at eleven months old. If your child is on an alternate vaccine schedule, you may use this time to catch up on a few vaccines. The next big well visit will be after his first birthday. This is a time of great transition for many babies, and you will likely have numerous questions for your child's doctor. Start keeping a list now of questions as they come up. There's so much going on at the twelve-month checkup, and you don't want to forget any of your questions.

If you have big concerns about something such as speech delay or developmental delay, or are concerned about frequent illnesses or other medical problems, make an appointment this month to discuss these issues. Your child's pediatrician will have a lot of basics that she needs to discuss with you at the twelve-month visit. In order to leave plenty of time for those important topics, it would be best to make an extra appointment now if you feel your child has major issues that need attention.

Common Questions You May Have This Month

My baby is eleven months old now. Can't we just go ahead and switch her from formula to whole milk? It's only a month away.

This is always tempting for parents, especially when you're so close to the one-year mark. If baby is ten and a half months old, you need to go buy more formula. If baby is between eleven and twelve months old, then the truth is it probably doesn't matter. Especially if baby is just one or two weeks away from his birthday, it really doesn't make sense to go stock up on formula. Now, that is the "laid-back doctor" answer. If you prefer to do things absolutely "by the book," the *best* thing is for baby to stay on breast milk or formula for a full twelve months. Cow's milk is a low source of iron, and babies who are transitioned too early are at risk for anemia and miss out on numerous other vitamins and minerals as well.

My baby has been exclusively breastfed since birth, but now my milk supply is dwindling. Can I supplement with whole milk? I hate the idea of giving him formula.

This is another big challenge for moms. I usually give breastfeeding moms the same advice as I give formula-feeding moms. If baby is only ten and a half months or so, you should probably supplement with formula, not whole milk. If baby is closer to eleven and a half months, you can probably get by supplementing with cow's milk. Again, the best thing for baby is to have an iron-rich source of milk for at least one year.

My baby fell and hit his head an hour ago. Now he seems sleepy. Should I be worried?

The short answer is "maybe." Now, this is sometimes a tough call. Your baby may still be taking a nap two or three times per day. If he hits his head and then an hour later seems sleepy, what are you supposed to do? Is it because he has a bad head injury, or is he just exhausted from having such a fun day and it's two o'clock (his regular nap time)? I remember seeing this scenario several times when I was working the ER during residency. The best advice I can give is to use your mama instinct. You know your child better than anyone else in the world. If you have any worries at all, it's always better to have him checked out. Trust me, the doctor will be just as glad as you are if it's a false alarm.

My baby fell and hit his head, but there's no bump there. I heard that if there's no bump on the outside, it means that the damage is inside instead. Is this true?

I've heard this fear from lots of parents. I don't know of any studies proving that this is this case. It seems to be an untrue fear for most cases. If you don't see a large bump or bruise, it's probably because the injury just wasn't as bad as you thought it sounded or looked. The same rules hold true, though, that were mentioned earlier in the chapter. If baby is excessively sleepy, or is excessively irritable, or has any other concerning signs (vomiting, abnormal coordination, unusual breathing), you should have him evaluated right away—even if you cannot see a bruise. If he loses consciousness at any time, even briefly, you should notify a doctor immediately.

Truth for the Journey

*"Blessed is the man who trusts in the LORD, whose confidence is in him.
He will be like a tree planted by the water that sends out its roots by the stream.
It does not fear when heat comes; its leaves are always green. It has no worries
in a year of drought and never fails to bear fruit."* Jeremiah 17:7–8

Your sweet baby is almost a year old. Can you believe it? You've been through a lot in the past eleven months, mama—breastfeeding woes (and hopefully triumph), sleepless nights, teething, and lots and lots of poop. As baby gets closer to his first birthday, I hope you are feeling more like a family now that he's grown from an infant to a little person, complete with a unique personality.

My heart for you this month is to encourage the establishment of your family and your home. Our key verse is from the book of Jeremiah. As the prophet sought to lead God's people from their wicked and unfruitful ways, he declares a prophetic word in chapter 17 that differentiates those who trust in man from those who trust in God. "Blessed is the man who trusts in the Lord, whose confidence is in him. He will be a like a tree planted by the water that sends out its roots by the stream." What a beautiful picture of family. Those who trust the Lord and put their confidence in him will establish deep and well-hydrated roots—they never fail to bear fruit.

Do you desire this fruitfulness for your family? Whether this is your first baby, or you already have one child (or a few) in your home, you are a family. Whether you are married or are a single mother, you are a family.

Isaiah 32:17 says, "The fruit of righteousness will be peace; the effect of righteousness will be quietness and confidence forever." Do you desire confidence in leading your family? Do you desire peace in your home? It starts with the righteousness that comes from a life in Christ. It's important to remember, though, that righteousness does not mean perfection. It's easy to get caught in this trap, especially as a new mom who desires to do everything right. We've discussed this throughout the year, and I pray you've been able to grasp the reality that perfection should never be the goal. Righteousness and effectiveness are about the heart, not the achievement of a desired outcome. When you diligently seek God on your family's behalf, you will experience quietness and confidence forever. Now is the perfect time to contend for this fruit as your child begins to go to lengths of spirit and activity you've never seen before.

There may be times, however, when you feel as though you don't know what to do. I just spent the morning chasing my wild little thirteen-month-old boy while disciplining my strong-willed, sassy four-year-old girl. When the house finally became quiet, I sat down, exhausted, wanting nothing more than to shut my eyes. I wanted to use the quietness to pray, but all I could muster was, *What should I do, Lord?* I desired so deeply to pray a fervent and poignant prayer for each of my children that would reveal to me exactly how to lead and guide them while taming their wild hearts. But alas, no such prayer came to mind. All I felt led to do was get up, turn on the computer, and begin typing. So here I am. Shortly after I sat down to write, I was reminded of another promise in Isaiah 30: "Whether you turn to the right or to the left, your ears will hear a voice behind you, saying, 'This is the way; walk in it'" (v. 21). Even when we come up against situations or decisions that paralyze us, even when we can't find the wherewithal to move, we can trust that if we listen, we will hear his voice, leading us in the way of fruitfulness.

Finding Your Mom Tribe

A few months ago, I attended a new mom's luncheon at my church. What a wonderful idea our leadership had to gather together the fifteen or more mommies in our body who gave birth in the past twelve months. Some were first-time moms and some, like me, already had children. We sat around and swapped breastfeeding and poop stories while getting to know one another and our little ones. It didn't matter our level of experience—each one had suggestions and new ideas to offer the group. Our pastor's wife and children's pastor both encouraged us to keep in touch, plan playgroups, and continue to fellowship. We are all part of a shared community, and this group will become our "mom tribe"—fellow mommies who dwell and learn together.

I've had the great privilege of having peer moms surrounding me since I became one myself. I don't know what I would do without my best mommy friends to call on weekly, sometimes daily. The camaraderie that develops when walking through a season as tough as motherhood is invaluable. Even if you do things slightly different than your other mothering friends, there is still so much to learn from one another. You may do nothing more than offer each other an empathetic "I hear ya, girl!" when sharing challenges and frustrations. This simple sisterhood may be the very thing that carries you through to high school graduation.

If you haven't already, I encourage you to find a mom tribe in your area. If you feel like you are the only one in this stage of life in your church or city, I assure you, you are not. There have got to be some other women keeping that OB office in business! You may not immediately click with women you find in your area. After all, relationships must be invested in and cultivated. But this is one of the most important things you can do for your child and for yourself. Here are a few suggestions for finding your mom tribe.

Ask the leaders in your church to connect you with other new moms. Start with the children's pastor. He or she should be able to introduce you to other moms of babies.

Look for an established group such as MOPS in your town. These groups meet once or twice a month and usually provide child care for a small fee.

Visit meetup.com to check for local playgroups. Message the group leader for an introduction and details.

Check with your local library for story times. Lots of moms attend these free events, so it's the perfect place to connect with others in your area.

Don't be afraid to strike up a conversation with another mom while your kids are playing at the park. Some of the best connections can be made around the jungle gym.

I am saying a special prayer today that you will be able to find your mom tribe and connect quickly for support and friendship. Finding support may be one of the smartest and most important things you do as a mom.

The First Birthday Bash

I'd bet my child's college savings (though it's not much of a prize at this point) that you have already been on Pinterest, salivating over the overachieving displays of children's birthday party paraphernalia. Admit it. I do it, too. We pin every single idea we come across, hoping to find the time and creativity to mimic the fabulous efforts of the mom who blogged it. If you are one of those moms who easily achieves such goals—please, tell me your secret. For most of us, Pinterest-worthy parties are an unattainable dream. So let me encourage you. Your child is not going to remember the matching fabric banner and cupcake toppers. He will not care one bit if the invitations came from Wal-Mart or Etsy. Those social graces speak only to our hearts, moms. They make us feel crafty and creative and hopefully the envy of every other mom in our playgroup. But they will not do anything for the precious child we are celebrating. So do yourself and your baby a favor and save the over-achieving party plans for when he is old enough to care. Plan a simple party with family and a few close friends. Savor the moment he takes his first bite of cake and opens his first birthday present. Take the pressure off so you don't miss out on the real joy of celebrating your child's life and your accomplishments as a mom. If you decide to go all out, by all means do it. Just make sure you invite me!

As you head into the last month of your baby's first year, I pray your confidence will come from above, my friend. Not from your family or friends, your spouse, or even the smiles of your sweet baby (although those are nice). Only your Heavenly Father can offer you enough acceptance to saturate the depths of a heart that longs for approval. Find your righteousness and peace in him alone and live in quietness and confidence forever.

Prayer Concerns

Upcoming transitions

Continued mobile and language development

Godly confidence

Mom friends

A Prayer for This Month

Dear Lord,

We are on the brink of so many transitions. I trust that you will go before us and pave the way for a peaceful crossing into the toddler years. Continue to guide my baby's development as he begins to walk and talk. I know that sure confidence can only come from you. I summon it now, more than ever before, Lord. I ask for you to deepen my friendships and provide new ones that will carry me through my days as a mom. May I be a blessing to other moms as we support each other during this season. Thank you for the sweet connection and fellowship we will have. Amen.

Write your own prayer of reflection.

_____

_____

_____

_____

_____

_____

_____

_____

_____

_____

_____

Journal

_____

_____

_____

_____

_____

_____

_____

_____

_____

_____

_____

A Year in the Making

Baby Stats

By twelve months, babies range from 17.25 to 26 pounds (7.8–11.8 kg) in weight and approximately 28 to 31.5 inches (72–80 cm) in length.

Development Checker at Twelve Months

Typical Skills

- ❑ Looks for origin of sounds
- ❑ Responds to own name
- ❑ Has a well-established pincer grasp
- ❑ Looks to where you point
- ❑ Cruises along furniture well
- ❑ Takes a few steps alone or walking
- ❑ Bangs two blocks together
- ❑ Drinks from a cup
- ❑ Indicates needs with gestures
- ❑ Becomes anxious or cries when parents leave
- ❑ Waves bye-bye and plays peekaboo
- ❑ Imitates sounds and expressions
- ❑ Says "mama" and "dada" and often a few other words
- ❑ Finds a hidden object
- ❑ Uses objects for correct purpose (holding phone to ear, putting comb in hair, and so on)

Concerning Signs

- ❑ Says no purposeful words
- ❑ Will not point at what he wants
- ❑ Never looks at you when you call his name
- ❑ Doesn't make eye contact

Language

Finally! You can enjoy hearing your baby call "mama" and "dada" as he squeals with delight over his birthday cake. He will now intentionally use these words to refer to you. He may also know a few other words, such as "uh-oh" or "bye-bye." It is expected for a baby to know a minimum of one word at this age. If he is not making any intentional words, inform your pediatrician, as this is a sign of developmental delay. Avoid using baby talk with your child so he can learn proper words and pronunciation as his ability to speak increases. Name objects consistently, and continue to describe what you are doing in detail to your child. This will increase his language skills dramatically.

Now is a wonderful time to introduce your baby to a second language. While a baby can be immersed in another language right from the start (especially if it is regularly spoken in the home), now is the time to use it more purposefully—begin referring to objects in both languages, for example.

Movement

Your baby should be cruising along furniture well at this point. He may be comfortable taking a few steps alone or may actually be walking by his birthday. This level of mobility opens up a whole new set of needs for a child, so don't rush him. Many babies do not walk proficiently for another few months. Let your baby lead the pace at which he begins to walk. If it takes him a bit longer to get the hang of it, you can enjoy a few more months before the chaos ensues.

As baby moves from cruising to taking a few wobbly steps to walking proficiently, he will need lots of practice. Get down on the floor with another family member and allow your child to practice walking back and forth between the two of you. The joy on your little one's face as he proudly moves from one loved one to another will be priceless. Make sure to affirm him boldly as he makes strides and comfort him when he falls.

If your child is walking, it means that he will fall—often. This stage will require even more of your undivided attention, mom, as baby will not be satisfied sitting still. His desire to roam and explore is exploding, leaving you to chase him as he does.

Refer back to Month Eleven for information on what to do if your child falls and how to know if he needs immediate medical attention.

Social Interaction

Separation anxiety. As mentioned last month, your baby is at the peak of separation anxiety now. He may become anxious and cry every time you leave the room. Although you will be tempted to extend your departure, remember that leaving the room quickly after an adequate good-bye is best at this age. Don't linger or wait for baby to be all right with your leaving. Chances are, he'll calm down a few minutes after you are gone and his attention is diverted to his caregiver or a new toy.

Your baby may love to wave bye-bye now. Although he cries when you leave the room, he'll enjoy waving bye-bye to others and may do so often. This happy gesture, which may look like a simple wave or a bold, hand-flapping motion, is one of the sweetest indications that baby is becoming more social. His ability to play games such as peekaboo is also increasing. He may hide behind an object or place his hands over his eyes now to engage you in this timeless amusement.

Encourage pretend play with dolls and common household objects. Baby will soon learn to pick up just about anything and hold it to his ear like a phone. Just be careful—if he starts to pretend he's texting all the time, it may be a sign you should put down your smartphone.

Spend some one-on-one time with your child every day. Working parents in particular may find that when they get home from work, there are certain household tasks that have to be done. But these responsibilities can quickly eat away at those few precious hours you have between getting home and baby's early bedtime. The laundry, dishes, and cleanup can wait. Focus on baby first and give yourself thirty minutes to complete household tasks after baby is asleep and before you spend some much-deserved time on yourself.

Discipline. It's important to recognize that children have a limited ability to understand consequences at this age. Be consistent about setting limits; learn to redirect your child from unwanted behaviors to something that is acceptable rather than punishing him. A child may not understand the concept of time-out just yet. Do not smack or spank your child—this usually backfires, especially at this age, as your young child may instead learn to hit others.

Lovies. Your child may become attached to a special blanket or toy around this time. Many moms and caregivers refer to these comfort items as "lovies." It is perfectly normal and acceptable for your toddler to show this type of preference and connection to something that comforts him. His lovey may be a wonderful tool in settling him when he feels stressed or afraid. You may also find his lovey to be a good replacement for a pacifier.

Weaning the pacifier. Although it is not required that your child give up his paci just yet, you may begin thinking about the separation now. Many dentists agree that a pacifier is still not harmful to a child's teeth, even at one year old. Most would recommend weaning the pacifier sometime between one and two years old. How and when a toddler gives up the paci will vary greatly from child to child. Start out slowly if you need to, allowing the paci only at bedtime and naptime for a few months. Eventually, your child will become less and less dependent on this comfort until you can remove it completely from his routine.

Baby Care
Feeding

Transitioning to milk. Moms who have been breastfeeding for the first year may want to wean their child from the breast at twelve months, even if only for part of the day. However, you may absolutely continue breastfeeding past one year of age. When to stop nursing is a personal decision and will look different for every family. Do not feel like you have to stop breastfeeding just because your child turns one. There is no right or wrong answer to when you should stop nursing. Children will sometimes naturally wean themselves about this time anyway, so don't let it hurt your feelings if your child is just as happy drinking from a cup as he is from your breast.

If you have decided to wean your child, the AAP recommends switching to whole (Vitamin D) milk at twelve months of age. If your baby has been formula-fed up to this point, now is the time to transition to regular milk. For non-breastfed children, daily milk intake should be 16 to 24 ounces of milk per day. Do not use low fat or skim milk. Your child needs the higher fat content for his continuing brain development. If your family is vegan, you may choose rice milk or almond milk. Rice milk and almond milk have lower protein contents than whole cow's milk and also have lower amounts of some vitamins (A, B, and C, for example), so you will need to make sure your child receives these vital nutrients from other sources.

Some children have no problem switching from formula or breast milk to whole milk, while others require a little more coaxing. If you try to switch "cold turkey," do not be surprised if your child refuses to drink milk at first. My own son took a while to transition. He was used to drinking very warm formula from a bottle, so ice-cold milk straight from the fridge wasn't something he was going to tolerate. We had to warm his milk for several months, and then he slowly got used to drinking cooler milk. We also mixed his milk with formula at first so that the change in flavor was not as sudden. We mixed half milk and half prepared formula to start, then slowly used up our last bit of formula by adding less and less each time. These two tricks may work well for you, too, during the transition.

It is not recommended to wean from a bottle to a sippy cup and change from formula or breast milk to cow's milk at the same time. Though some children can tolerate the double switch, the majority of the children I've seen simply stop drinking milk if this is done. Pick one or the other, and after your child has mastered the first goal, go on to the next. There is no rush to make the transition overnight.

Encourage your child to drink water every day now. Continue to limit juice to no more than 6 ounces per day, if you choose to offer it at all.

Most children will eat three small meals and two snacks per day. Remember, a "meal" at this age may consist of only a few tablespoons of food. Offer nutritious foods to your child and avoid the temptation of giving snacks and "junk" just so that he'll eat something. Continue to avoid foods that are choking hazards such as hot dogs, grapes (unless cut up), and carrots (unless softened and cut). Do not force your child to finish everything on his plate.

Best Foods for a One-Year-Old

Your baby is quickly becoming a toddler, and he's ready for a more "sophisticated" menu. There are many foods that are good to feed your child at this stage, but having a list of go-to items will help you plan. Below you will find our list of recommended foods for a one-year-old child, plus a sample menu to give you an idea of how food might be spaced throughout the day. Keep in mind that your child may vary in the types of foods and the amount of food he eats. His favorite food one day might be refused the next. While you may be consumed with the desire to make sure your child eats enough healthy food daily, it is more important at this stage to establish consistent meal times and introduce new, nutritious foods to cultivate a love for healthy eating.

Whole grains. Serve your child oatmeal, soft bread, whole wheat pasta, or Cheerios. Make sure pasta is soft and cut small enough to avoid choking.

Protein. Chicken, white fish, ground turkey, beans, and eggs are all great sources of protein for your child.

Dairy. In addition to his regular schedule of whole (or breast) milk, your child may enjoy yogurt and soft cheeses cut into small pieces that are easy to pick up.

Fruit. Bananas, berries, and applesauce are typical favorites at this age. Your child may not like the shock of many citrus fruits, but that does not mean you shouldn't keep trying. Be careful with hard fruits such as apples that may still be a choking hazard.

Veggies. Avocados, carrots, corn, peas, green beans, and sweet potatoes are great vegetables to offer at this stage. Be careful of veggies with too much texture, such as broccoli, unless you puree it to a smooth texture.

Your child will love bite-sized foods that are easy to pick up. Many toddlers do not want to be spoon-fed any longer by this time. Encourage his independence by serving him foods he can easily feed himself. Fruits and vegetables can be purchased fresh or frozen. It is easiest and most cost effective to serve frozen fruits and veggies. You can thaw just a teaspoon or two at a time and will be able to store remaining food without having to use it up quickly as with fresh foods.

Sample Menu for a One-Year-Old

Early morning – 5 ounces of milk upon waking
Breakfast – oatmeal with berries, water
Snack – applesauce and graham crackers, 5 ounces of milk
Lunch – whole grain pasta with peas and ground turkey, water
Snack – avocado, small pieces of cheese, 5 ounces of milk
Dinner – baked chicken, steamed (soft) carrots, sweet potato, bites of whole wheat
   bread, water
Bedtime – 6 ounces of milk

Introducing sugar. Once your child experiences the taste of sugar on his tongue, there is no going back. Although you should definitely not deprive him the joy of his first birthday cake, be careful how much sugar you allow your child outside of this acceptable rite of passage. Reserve any treats for truly special occasions, or you risk starting a habit that is hard to break.

Sleep and Schedules

Most children still take two naps per day but may transition to one any time after their first birthday. Many toddlers will not drop to one nap until at least eighteen months. If your baby is only taking one nap a day right now, it may not be enough. Just because baby *can* get by with a single ninety-minute nap doesn't mean he *should*. You may find that he becomes cranky and gets easily frustrated if he is not well-rested. Work on getting a good nap routine reestablished. This is particularly difficult if you have errands to run or a different schedule every day. Try to reserve certain hours of the day for staying at home and making sure your child is well-rested.

You will know your child is ready to drop to one nap when he begins to take longer to fall asleep for his morning nap or if he sleeps so long in the morning that he has difficulty settling down in the afternoon. Either of these indicators may mean your toddler is ready to adjust his nap schedule to one rest time. When you make the transition to one nap, keep in mind that the remaining nap may not be at the same time he has been sleeping up until this point. You may need to simply push back his morning nap bit by bit until it falls at mid-day or early afternoon.

If your child is in day care or mother's day out, they may have set nap times, and he'll adjust to their schedule. As your child transitions his schedule between twelve and eighteen months, be aware that his bedtime may need to adjust as well. Pay attention to his cues, and you'll figure out how to adjust to meet his needs.

Diapering

Children are typically not developmentally ready for toilet training until twenty-four months of age. The earliest I would recommend an attempt at toilet training would be eighteen months, and even then it would be accomplished in only a small percentage of children. Be patient. Although the idea of giving up diapers is appealing, potty-trained children come with a whole new set of responsibilities. The older they are, the more smooth your transition will be. Give it time.

Teething

Your child may have as many as eight teeth by his first birthday. Continue to brush your child's teeth after meals and before bedtime. Remember, if toothpaste is used, find a product that does not contain added fluoride.

Baby Safety

Now that baby is completely mobile, it's important to take safety precautions to the next level. Much of this information has been covered before in this book, but it bears repeating as you consider your toddler's newfound freedom and tenacity. It should go without saying, but make sure you have guns locked up and out of reach of all children in your home.

Baby gates. Although you may not use a play yard or baby gate in your living room to contain your toddler, keeping gates on stairs is still a must. Make sure your gates are securely installed and locked at the top and bottom of your stairs, as your toddler may soon learn to open them. Make sure older children realize the importance of always closing the gate behind them.

Kitchen safety. Be careful with hot liquids. Make sure that handles of pots and pans on the stove are turned inward so your child cannot reach up and grab one, spilling hot food on himself. Knives, medications, heavy objects, and cleaning supplies are particularly hazardous at this age. Keep these items locked away and well out of reach.

Bath safety. Always provide direct supervision of your child, especially while bathing. It only takes a few seconds for your child to figure out a way to get into trouble. It can be so tempting to walk away just for a minute to answer the phone or to see who is ringing the doorbell. Especially now that baby can pull to stand (but is still clumsy), he could stand up, slip, and bonk his head on the faucet or tub. Children can drown in just a few inches of water. If you must answer the phone or the door, it's better to wrap baby up and take him with you.

Furniture. Make sure that bookshelves, furniture, and televisions are securely mounted. Children love to climb and can easily overturn objects and hurt themselves.

Car seat. Remember, the current AAP recommendations state that all infants and toddlers should ride rear-facing in the back seat until two years of age. This recommendation is more cautious than most state laws. Legally, in most states, you can turn baby's car seat to front-facing after baby's first birthday if he weighs twenty pounds. But studies have shown that staying rear-facing for longer prevents serious injury or death in the case of an accident. Pay close attention to manufacturer height and weight guidelines for your seat, as your child is in a season of growth and may outgrow his seat sooner than you think.

There is no brand of car seat that is the "best." Just because a car seat has a higher price does not mean it is safer than a lower-priced car seat. If you are fortunate enough to have a certified car seat technician in your town, it is recommended to have them check baby's car seat for proper installation. It doesn't seem like installing a car seat is rocket science, but it's harder than it looks to do it properly. My husband and I are both bright, well-educated people, so we thought surely we could manage to put in a simple little car seat. Wrong. We had our son's infant car

("AAP Updates Recommendations on Car Seats" and "Car Seats: Information for Families for 2012," healthychildren.org.)

seat and then his convertible car seat checked by the CPS technician in our town, and to our surprise, we had installed both of them improperly. It pays to have your seat double-checked by an expert.

Expectations for Your Doctor Visits

The twelve-month well-child checkup is one of the most anticipated. What a difference a year makes! For most parents, it is hard to imagine their lives before their child arrived. Your doctor will expect your child to have mastered many skills by this age, including first words and maybe even first steps. The primary focus of this well visit will be to make sure that baby is developmentally on track. Your child's pediatrician will look for delays in motor skills, cognitive development, language development, and social skills. Developmental delays are most successfully treated with early intervention.

Autism

At each of your baby's well visits, your doctor has been assessing for early signs of autism. Autism spectrum disorders (ASDs) affect a child's language, social, and learning abilities. No one knows what causes ASDs. Most experts agree that early signs of autism occur well before a child's first birthday, though they may be subtle. ASDs include pervasive developmental disorder (PDD), Asperger's syndrome, and autistic disorder.

A child with the earliest signs of autism spectrum disorder may:

· Not like to be cuddled like other children.
· Not make eye contact with you.
· Not smile back at you or smile less than expected.
· Not respond to his name being called.
· Not respond to someone speaking to him ("tuning out"), though able to hear other sounds well.
· Not use hand gestures, especially not point out an object and try to get your attention to see it, too.

If you have had any of these concerns in this first year, you should tell your child's doctor so she can screen him for autism spectrum disorder.

If your child did not have screening labs for anemia at his nine-month visit, it will likely be done at the twelve-month checkup. In addition, your child's doctor may perform a lead-level screen if it has not already been done at a prior visit.

Your baby is also due for vaccines at this visit. Each office gives vaccines on a slightly different schedule, but you can expect anywhere from two to four immunizations at the twelve-month checkup. These immunizations may include your child's first varicella (chickenpox) and MMR (measles, mumps, rubella) vaccines. He may also receive a first dose of hepatitis A vaccine. Other vaccines that may be given include a final dose of hepatitis B (if he has not yet had a third dose) or a booster dose of DTaP and Hib. Some of these shots can be given at his fifteen-month checkup as well depending on your doctor's recommendations. If you are choosing to use an alternate schedule, discuss your concerns with your child's doctor and make a plan to complete the vaccines as you feel comfortable. Remember, your child is susceptible for as long as vaccines are delayed. In recent years, there have been increasing outbreaks of illnesses such as measles and pertussis. Consider these and other illnesses that have been more prevalent when you are choosing which vaccines to give now versus later.

Common Questions You May Have This Month

My child is all over the place since he's learned to walk. What is considered normal behavior for a one-year-old?

Your baby is likely to be interested in everything he shouldn't touch. If you can think of something in your dining room that is off-limits, you can bet that's the first thing he'll want. Work on redirecting him to toys and activities that are acceptable and safe. Your baby is turning into a toddler, and toddlers are all about movement and exploration. He's very likely to prefer walking on his own instead of being held or carried. He may fight against his stroller or the shopping cart and instead want to be down moving around on his own. Try to make shopping trips brief and when he is well-rested. You'll have fewer tantrums to deal with this way.

My child is already a "picky eater." How can I make sure he's getting adequate nutrition now that I'm not breastfeeding?

For starters, don't be afraid to offer your child a particular food again even if he didn't care for it the first time. Toddlers can be a finicky bunch. Your child's favorite food may be completely different next month. He may only eat bananas today and then refuse them by next week. Continue to offer a variety of foods at every meal. Don't make your child a completely different meal from your own every time. Share food from your plate. If he sees you eating carrots, he's much more likely to eat them, too. Most cereals and breads are fortified with vitamins and minerals, so a mixture of grains, fruits, and vegetables will provide a good variety of nutrients. Milk is very important for baby's growing body as well. If you are struggling to get in at least 16 ounces of milk per day, be sure to offer yogurt and other calcium-rich foods to help offset the lack of milk.

Mommy Care
Planning for the Next Baby

With all of my patients, as they enter the third trimester, I discuss what their contraceptive plans are for after the baby is born.

Many smile a beautiful, blissful, glowingly pregnant smile and say, "Oh, no. I don't think we will ever use contraception again. Hopefully we will get pregnant again right away!"

Fast-forward to their postpartum visit. A sleep-deprived, exhausted new mom sits before me. Her first topic of conversation: contraception. While she is madly in love with her new baby, the thought of having another one right away is a little overwhelming. She is not physically ready to go down that road again.

Some women are ready right away. I once had a women ask me at delivery when she could try for another baby. My answer: "Well, you at least have to wait for me to get the placenta out!"

The decision of when to try for your next child depends on many factors. Finances, age, personal goals, and beliefs on contraception are just a few. From a medical standpoint, according to studies looking at pregnancy outcomes, it is best to conceive eighteen months to four years after your last delivery.

I find it interesting that the "optimal" time for conception of the next child is about eighteen months, since this is when children are truly at their most adorable—full of toothy grins and giggles as they toddle around. This stage of ultimate cuteness entices people to have another baby. They then proceed to conceive before their child hits the terrific twos (which, while adorable, is a challenging time).

Pregnancies conceived less than eighteen months since the last delivery have an increased risk of preterm delivery and low birth weight. Pregnancy takes a lot out of your body, and it takes time for a woman to recover from the stress and for her nutrient supplies to get back to normal. The theory is that the body has not fully recovered at less than eighteen months, putting the baby at risk of not growing as well (low birth weight). The risk of preterm delivery is further amplified in teens who conceive again quickly, since teens have often used their nutritional supplies on their own growth as well as their baby's.

Women who attempted a trial of labor after a cesarean section have an increased risk of uterine rupture if the pregnancies are less than eighteen months apart.

Pregnancies conceived less than twelve months since the last delivery have an increased rate of placental abnormalities, such as placenta previa and placental abruption. Placenta previa is a condition where the placenta covers the opening of the cervix, making vaginal delivery unsafe and increasing the risk of hemorrhage. Placental abruption occurs when the placenta begins to detach from the uterus before the baby is delivered. It can result in hemorrhage and fetal distress.

Pregnancies conceived less than six months from delivery have an increased rate of neural tube defects and autism. Neural tube defect is associated with low maternal folate levels, so most likely in pregnancies less than six months apart, the mother has not had time to fully replenish those supplies.

Pregnancies conceived more than four years from the last delivery have an increased rate of preeclampsia, fetal growth restriction, and cesarean section. It is not clear why this increased risk is seen other than the possible health changes in the mom over this time.

The actual "increased risk" in each of the cases is statistically significant but overall is low for the average woman. Take preterm delivery: the risk increase with conceiving early is 20 percent. For the average mom with no history of preterm birth, this changes her risk from 1 percent to 1.2 percent, which is negligible. However, a woman with a previous preterm delivery sees her risk go from 15 percent to 18 percent. These increased risks are most significant for those moms who already have risk factors for these conditions.

For the average healthy mom with no medical problems and a vaginal delivery, the increased risks of these complications with conceiving again soon are extremely low. Women with a cesarean section should wait eighteen months for their scar to fully heal, especially if they desire a trial of labor (VBAC). Those with a history of the pregnancy complications listed above are advised to wait the suggested interval before conceiving.

Lots of prayer and being on the same page as your spouse should be at the forefront when you are making the decision about when to have another child. But knowing the medical facts is equally important for making sure you are ready— both body and mind—to grow your family.

A Real-Life Story

Adoptive Mom to Twins

Tiffany – Mom to Livi, Emily, and Addie (big sis)

It was December 14, 2009, when we got the call that would change our lives forever. It was our contact from Mercy Ministries, the ministry from which we originally intended to adopt. She asked me how our international adoption plan was going. After waiting more than a year to be chosen by a birth mom through Mercy, we decided to try an international plan. I explained that we were waiting on one final paper and then we would be locked in to a Bulgarian adoption. She proceeded to tell me one of their birth moms had chosen us. I was in complete shock. She explained about the baby having a kidney issue, and shared the birth mom's story.

After a twenty-minute conversation she dropped the bigger news: it was TWINS! I had to sit down for that one. We made a plan to talk with the birth mom later that week. There I was with my daughter's big brown eyes staring up at me, asking, "Mommy, what was that?" I explained to her about the call, and a birth mom choosing us. Her response was, "You mean she chose me to be the big sister?" It was precious.

The next few weeks are a blur. We met the birth mom for lunch, had phone calls, and spent some time with her. We loved her instantly. God connected so many of our stories, and we knew his hand was all over our times together. After the girls were born, she struggled again with her decision to place them. The pain and agony of seeing your two beautiful babies raised, loved, and adored by someone else was just too much. We prayed diligently for her and asked God for his will to be done in all of our lives. After a week, she made her decision. She walked into the office at Mercy and said, "I know that I know that I know the girls are supposed to be theirs."

When I walked into the hospital to meet the twins for the first time, I just didn't know how I would feel. *Would I fall in love at first sight? Would I feel bonded to them? Would I feel like they were someone else's babies? Would I be able to tell them apart? Would I know what to do?* It was definitely love at first sight. For those who have adopted, you know how it goes. The Lord gives you a supernatural experience. It is almost surreal. I just didn't know I was capable of feeling the way I did that day. Maybe it was realizing that the end of the dark journey of infertility and loss was imminent. Maybe it was knowing this was God's plan all along.

Life with twins is an adventure every day. Is it hard? Oh my, YES! Is it totally worth it? YES! To tell the truth, if I could choose again to have two babies or one, I would choose two. The relationship they have with each other is precious and they never have to be alone, which is particularly great when leaving them with other people. The most difficult thing for me has been the sheer physical exhaustion of lifting two babies and caring for them. It was a difficult adjustment for all of us, but also a natural one. To be honest, I think becoming a mom for the first time was more difficult for me than the adjustment to twins. My biological daughter, Addie, has been a wonderful big sister, but her adjustment was difficult, too. When you are in public with identical twins, people are so excited to see them that siblings are often ignored. It's been important for me to give her extra attention from time to time.

All in all, some days are much more demanding than I ever thought, but the blessings far outweigh the challenges. The best advice I can give moms of twins is, take it one day at a time and don't be afraid to ask for help, especially in the early days.

Our birth mom is an amazing young woman, who has given us something more wonderful than I could ever imagine giving anyone. We are able to keep in touch with her regularly and see her as often as we can. Our decision to allow her into our lives, our home, and the girls' lives was easy. After having so many friends who were adopted, I decided the more truth the girls knew the better for everyone. It is just indescribable how much love, appreciation, gratefulness, and respect we have for her. She is our hero.

After four and a half *long* years of failed IVFs, miscarriages, ectopic pregnancies, corrective surgery, and loss, this was our answer. The one God had all along. If we had only known that all the tears and pain and loss was not for nothing. He was just waiting to give us his answer. The road of waiting is so painful. It was the hardest time in our lives. We spent so much time wondering if our daughter would ever have a sibling, if God would ever answer our prayers. When we held our precious girls for the first time, all the pain was washed away in one moment.

God is good. For any of you walking through dark and painful valleys, please remember, it is not the end of the story. It is just the road leading to God's perfect plan.

Truth for the Journey

"I thank Christ Jesus our Lord, who has given me strength, that he considered me trustworthy, appointing me to his service." 1 Timothy 1:12

You did it! You made it through your baby's first year. I'm sure you'll agree it was one of the hardest things (besides labor) you've ever done and the wildest ride you've ever been on. But it was fun and sweet and joy-filled . . . and you survived. And not only did you survive—I bet you thrived much more than you even realize.

I hope in the midst of all of the parties and celebrations of your little one, you take some time to reflect back on how far you've come this year. I'm thinking about instituting a new holiday—the Mommiversary—a celebration of surviving and thriving baby's first year. Why should he get all the presents and cake? You changed the diapers and rocked him and fed him! I realize no mama is going to steal the spotlight from her precious child on his first birthday, but in all seriousness, I hope you find a way to reward yourself for the past year. Try to find a few hours one day to be by yourself. Get a massage or a mani/pedi and spend time thinking about how much you've accomplished, mom. It's fine to regret some things if you can do so without beating yourself up. Those lessons are valuable as you move forward in motherhood. Reflect on the past year, both good and bad, but in the end, be proud of yourself and go confidently into this next season.

Most importantly, I hope you will thank the Lord for entrusting you with the life of your baby. He considered you trustworthy of this calling. He knew you would be the perfect mom for your child. You have been and will continue to be for years to come. I pray that your achievements as a mom throughout baby's first year will give you all of the confidence you need to thrive as your child grows and as you consider adding another baby to your family.

Many moms are thinking about becoming pregnant again (if they are not already) at this point. Dr. Rupe shared a few great tips on preparing yourself physically for another baby. Getting your body prepared to grow another life is important. And preparing your heart and mind is just as crucial. Yes, having a baby changes everything. But having two may very well rock your world. (I know it did mine.) Seek the Lord with your spouse for his timing as it relates to growing your family. Do not (I repeat) do not get pregnant because all of your friends are having babies close together or it seems like the practical thing to do. Make sure you are ready to add another little person to your family. There is no perfect spacing between children. No matter what your timing, it will come with pros and cons. If you are called to have another child in this season, then you will have all the wisdom and grace you need available to you as you ask for it. "If any of you lacks wisdom, he should ask God, who gives generously to all without finding fault, and it will be given to him" (James 1:5). Seek his wisdom for your family, and trust that he will bring life at the appointed time.

Secondary Infertility

If you know my story, you know I struggled to conceive both of my children. If you did not encounter any challenges with your first baby but are unable to conceive a second child after a year of trying, you may be experiencing secondary infertility. According to RESOLVE, the National Infertility Association, "Secondary infertility is defined as the inability to become pregnant, or to carry a pregnancy to term, following the birth of one or more biological children. The birth of the first child does not involve any assisted reproductive technologies or fertility medications" ("Secondary Infertility," resolve.org). Just because you do not conceive as quickly as last time does not mean there is a problem. Talk to your doctor if you are frustrated or concerned. She can guide you in the best course of action. Most importantly, trust God for his perfect timing. I know it sounds cliché, but it's true. I would never have imagined the struggle and loss we'd encounter on our journey to becoming pregnant with my son, but I wouldn't change any of it. We grew in our faith, and in the end, God received all the glory for his miracle conception.

Your marriage is perhaps the most important thing to consider when thinking about having another child. Determine whether you and your spouse are on the same page about timing as you seek God for direction. Think about how having baby number one affected your relationship with your husband. Have you overcome the strain and settled into a good rhythm as a couple? Is there more work to be done or focus to be had on your relationship before adding the weight of another child? While you will never feel perfectly ready for one or any number of babies, make sure you both feel a sure peace about moving forward. Refer back to our discussion on marriage in Month Four and study the passage from Colossians 3 again as you pray about having another baby.

This has been an amazing year of growth for you, mama. You have successfully sustained another life for twelve months! It's no mistake that the first year of motherhood feels like a crash course of training. Much like a military boot camp, I am convinced if you can survive the sleepless nights, mounds of poop, and late afternoon crying spells, you can do anything. As we wrap up the year, let's look at some of the principles you can take with you into every season of your child's life.

- Seek godly wisdom – Proverbs 4:7
- Pursue peace – Psalm 34:14
- Avoid the comparison trap – 2 Corinthians 3:5
- Be careful what you read/listen to – James 3:17
- Practice gratitude – Colossians 3:15–17 in *The Message*

Focus on these key principles, mom, and you will do well in the years to come. Author Jill Churchill wrote, "There is no way to be a perfect mother, and a million ways to be a good one" (*Grime and Punishment*, Avon, 1992). This truth speaks to the fact that being a "good" mother will look different for each of us. I hope you have been able to settle this in your heart. Motherhood requires a finesse that is unique to each individual mother and only obtained through fervent prayer and daily experience. The goal is not perfection but rather progress.

As you look back over the past year, you will be able to see the progress you've made as a mom. That progress is a complete testament to your mothering ability. God considered you trustworthy, appointing you to this task, and you can believe he looks upon you now with great favor, saying, "Well done, my good and faithful servant."

Prayer Concerns

Transition to milk

Moving into toddler years

Wisdom for growing our family

A Prayer for This Month

Dear Lord,

What a privilege it has been to steward the gift of my child this past year. Thank you for considering me worthy and appointing me to the task of motherhood. I pray that through this role, I will bring glory to you daily. As we transition to the toddler years, I ask for continued wisdom and grace. Holy Spirit, lead and guide us just as you've done thus far. May I always seek progress over perfection, knowing that you are pleased with my efforts and cover my lack. Thank you for your faithfulness, Lord. Amen.

Write your own prayer of reflection.

_____

_____

_____

_____

_____

_____

_____

_____

_____

Journal

_____

_____

_____

_____

_____

_____

_____

_____

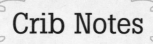
Crib Notes

Months Ten to Twelve

Mommy's Heart—Pray for the establishment of your home as baby grows. His personality is exploding, and he's beginning to fit into your lives more tangibly. Seek the fruit of righteousness for your home and confidence for your family (Isa. 32:17).

Baby's Development—Baby can crawl, scoot, and cruise your furniture. He may start walking during this stage. Your little one is on the move as he begins to explore his surroundings. He's likely saying "dada" or "mama" and other simple words. You are probably saying, "No, no!" often now.

Feeding—Breastfeeding: 15 to 30 minutes four times per day. Bottle-feeding: 16 to 24 ounces of milk. Plus, three meals and two snacks consisting of healthy baby and finger foods.

Sleeping—9 to 12 hours at night. One or two 30-minute to 2-hour naps.

Play—Read to your baby daily. This is one of the best forms of play and social interaction and will develop his language skills. Get on the floor with your little one and "race" from one end of the room to the other. He'll be so proud of his ability to "keep up." Utilize music and age-appropriate instruments in daily play.

Appendix

EDINBURGH POSTNATAL DEPRESSION SCALE (EPDS)

The EPDS was developed for screening postpartum women in outpatient, home visiting settings, or at the 6-8 week postpartum examination. The EPDS consists of 10 questions. Responses are scored 0, 1, 2, or 3 according to increased severity of the symptom. Items marked with an asterisk (*) are reverse scored (i.e., 3, 2, 1, and 0). The total score is determined by adding together the scores for each of the 10 items. Validation studies have utilized various threshold scores in determining which women were positive and in need of referral. Cut-off scores ranged from 9 to 13 points. Therefore, to err on safety's side, a woman scoring 9 or more points or indicating any suicidal ideation – that is she scores 1 or higher on question #10 – should be referred immediately for follow-up. Even if a woman scores less than 9, if the clinician feels the client is suffering from depression, an appropriate referral should be made. The EPDS is only a screening tool. It does not diagnose depression – that is done by appropriately licensed health care personnel.

Instructions for Users

1. The mother is asked to underline 1 of 4 possible responses that comes the closest to how she has been feeling the previous 7 days.
2. All 10 items must be completed.
3. Care should be taken to avoid the possibility of the mother discussing her answers with others.
4. The mother should complete the scale herself.

Name: _____   Date: _____

Address: _____   Baby's Age: _____

As you have recently had a baby, we would like to know how you are feeling. Please UNDERLINE the answer which comes closest to how you have felt IN THE PAST 7 DAYS, not just how you feel today.

Here is an example, already completed.
I have felt happy:
Yes, all the time
<u>Yes, most of the time</u>
No, not very often
No, not at all

This would mean: "I have felt happy most of the time" during the past week. Please complete the other questions in the same way.

In the past 7 days:

1. I have been able to laugh and see the funny side of things:
   As much as I always could
   Not quite so much now
   Definitely not so much now
   Not at all

2. I have looked forward with enjoyment to things:
   As much as I ever did
   Rather less than I used to
   Definitely less than I used to
   Hardly at all

*3. I have blamed myself unnecessarily when things went wrong:
   Yes, most of the time
   Yes, some of the time
   Not very often
   No, never

4. I have been anxious or worried for no good reason:
   No, not at all
   Hardly ever
   Yes, sometimes
   Yes, very often

*5. I have felt scared or panicky for no very good reason:
   Yes, quite a lot
   Yes, sometimes
   No, not much
   No, not at all

*6. Things have been getting on top of me:
   Yes, most of the time I haven't been able to cope at all
   Yes, sometimes I haven't been coping as well as usual
   No, most of the time I have coped quite well
   No, have been coping as well as ever

*7. I have been so unhappy that I have had difficulty sleeping:
   Yes, most of the time
   Yes, sometimes
   Not very often
   No, not at all

*8. I have felt sad or miserable:
   Yes, most of the time
   Yes, quite often
   Not very often
   No, not at all

*9. I have been so unhappy that I have been crying:
   Yes, most of the time
   Yes, quite often
   Only occasionally
   No, never

*10. The thought of harming myself has occurred to me:
   Yes, quite often
   Sometimes
   Hardly ever
   Never

EDINBURGH POSTNATAL DEPRESSION SCALE (EPDS)
J. L. Cox, J.M. Holden, R. Sagovsky
From: British Journal of Psychiatry (1987), 150, 782-786.

Date: _____

Baby's Daily Schedule Tracker

Time	Mood	Food Breast or Bottle			Sleep Down Up			Diaper Wet Soiled	
		Breast	Bottle		Down	Up		Wet	Soiled
9am	Tired	15 min on each side	4oz		9:45am	11am		✓	Soft

Notes/Questions for Pediatrician:

Vaccination Tracker

Month	Date	Vaccines Given	Baby's Response
Birth			
2			
4			
6			
12			

Visit www.thebabycompanion.com/schedule to download a full size copy.

Baby Gear Must Haves

Top 10 items the moms in our community could NOT live without:

- ☐ Muslin swaddle blankets
- ☐ Swing or bouncy seat
- ☐ Bulb syringe (from the hospital)
- ☐ Baby carrier or wrap
- ☐ Pacifier
- ☐ White noise machine
- ☐ Nursing pillow
- ☐ Humidifier
- ☐ A good stroller

Favorite tools for:

Babywearing

- ☐ Moby Wrap
- ☐ Ergo Baby Carrier
- ☐ Hot Sling

Relief for illness

- ☐ Hospital bulb syringe
- ☐ Nosefrida nasal aspirator
- ☐ Humidifier

Making baby food

- ☐ Baby Bullet System
- ☐ Pampered Chef Micro Cooker, small
- ☐ Good, old-fashioned food processor

Teething relief

- ☐ Hyland's Teething Tablets
- ☐ Gum massager

Fussiness/gas

- ☐ Grip water
- ☐ Simethicone drops

Clipping/filing baby's nails

- ☐ Tempered glass nail file
- ☐ Safety First Clear View nail clipper

Recommended Resources

Parenting/Postpartum
Healthychildren.org
Babycenter.com
Parenting.com
Healthy Children (App)
The AAP's Caring for Your Baby and Young Child: Birth to Age 5 by Dr. Steven P. Shelov
My Single Mom Life by Angela Thomas

Breastfeeding
lalecheleague.com
ilca.org
medela.com
bfmed.org
aafp.org
The Nursing Mother's Companion by Kathleen Huggins
Breastfeeding Your Baby: Answers to Common Questions by The American Academy of Pediatrics

Sleep and Scheduling
Sleepfoundation.org for sleep needs by age
Healthy Sleep Habits, Happy Child by Dr. Mark Weissbluth
Happiest Baby on the Block by Dr. Harvey Karp
The Essential Baby Organizer: Birth to One Year by Dani Rasmussen and Antoinette Perez
Baby Connect Activity Logger (App)
Baby Log (App)
Total Baby (App)
Sprout (App)
Eat Sleep (App)

Car Seat Installation and Safety
nhtsa.gov/Safety/CPS or call 888-327-4236
seatcheck.org or call 866-732-8243
cert.safekids.org or call 877-366-8154 to find a technician

Immunizations
Because most books on vaccination tend to be one-sided, we would not recommend any in particular. We advise moms to look to these trusted websites to read the facts about immunizations. While these sites do support vaccinating your child on schedule, we believe that the information is medically accurate and that it will allow you to make an informed decision for your family. Above all else, we encourage you to pray over this very important decision.
cdc.gov
healthychildren.org
immunize.org

Devotional Books/Websites
Jesus Calling by Sarah Young
Tender Mercy for a Mother's Soul by Angela Thomas
Choosing Joy by Angela Thomas
Our Daily Bread @ rbc.org
Hello Mornings @ inspiredtoaction.com
incourage.me
graceformoms.com
Jesus Calling (App)
You Version Bible (App)

Index

Our hope is that *The Baby Companion* has helped you take care of your baby and yourself throughout this year. Now you can give back to a mom who is in great need of prenatal and postnatal care as well as provide care for her new baby.

Compassion International's Child Survival Program offers prenatal care, health care, nutritional training, parenting-skills training and spiritual nurturing for mothers-to-be through special projects in countries such as Haiti, Kenya and Ecuador. The program also provides nutritious food, immunizations, ongoing health care and physical emotional and spiritual development activities for at-risk infants and young children. In short, these moms and babies get the holistic care they need—mind, body, soul and spirit—through a local church that understands their particular needs and that identifies those who need it most.

You can help save the lives of moms and babies with your tax-deductable monthly contribution of $20.

Visit graceformoms.com/compassion

Help rescue, nurture and disciple children during their critical early years, and give moms the confidence and knowledge they need to raise their little ones. Will you join us in giving back?

Releasing children from poverty
Compassion®
in Jesus' name

Now what?

Join our *community* of
moms like *you* at
thebabycompanion.com

Grow in *grace* with
moms of all stages at
graceformoms.com
it's ok, you're covered.